TABLE OF CONTENTS

PROBE/SENSOR TYPES VERSUS ACTIVITIES

Probe/Sensor Type	Used with Activities
TI light probe	7, 15, 22
TI temperature probe	10, 20, 21
TI voltage probe	12
Vernier CBL motion detector	1, 4, 5, 8, 9, 13, 16, 17, 18, 19, 24
Vernier student force sensor	2, 5, 25
Vernier microphone/amplifier	23
Vernier pressure sensor	3, 6, 11
Vernier pH meter system	14

FUNCTION TYPES VERSUS ACTIVITIES

Function Type	Studied in these Activities
Linear	2, 3, 4, 5, 11, 25
Inverse/Inverse Square	6, 7
Quadratic	8, 9
Exponential/Logarithmic	10, 12, 13, 14
Sinusoidal/Periodic	15, 16, 23
Second Degree Curves	17
Piecewise	18, 19
Statistical Plots	21, 22

ABOUT THE AUTHORS

Chris Brueningsen teaches math and physics at The Kiski School in Saltsburg, Pennsylvania. He has written a number of articles for math and science journals and is co-author of *Exploring Physics and Math with the CBL™ System*, a Texas Instruments publication.

Bill Bower is a teacher and Chairman of the Mathematics Department at The Kiski School. Throughout his 18-year career he has taught all levels of high-school math. In recent years, graphing calculator technology has become an integral part of his teaching.

Linda Antinone is the Master Advanced Placement Teacher for Science in the Dallas Public Schools. She received Ohio's Presidential Award for Excellence in Mathematics Teaching in 1993. She has taught math and science to students in grades 7 to 12.

Elisa Brueningsen has taught science and math at The Kiski School for the past three years. She has been using technology to connect these subjects and has brought real-world examples into the classroom from her background in research biology.

The authors are active in professional development programs for secondary math and science teachers at the local, state, and national levels. Most recently, their efforts have focused on the development of a summer technology workshop entitled, "Connecting Math and Science." This workshop is part of the family of Teachers Teaching with Technology Summer Institutes founded by Bert Waits and Frank Demana at the Ohio State University in 1988.

PREFACE

This workbook was designed to provide math students, from algebra through calculus, with a fun and exciting way to explore real-world applications of mathematical concepts. All of the activities incorporate the Texas Instruments Calculator-Based Laboratory™ (CBL™) System. This device is used to collect various kinds of data, such as motion, force, sound, light, and temperature. The TI-82 graphics calculator retrieves the data, then serves as a powerful analysis tool, helping students build mathematical models.

Each activity is presented in worksheet format. Background information, set-up diagrams, and general instructions are given for each activity. Ample space is provided for students to record data and complete easy-to-follow exercises with clear calculator keystrokes. "Extensions" and further applications are included in most activities to allow for advanced, independent investigations. Teacher information sheets supply helpful notes for completing the activities, as well as sample data plots and answers to student questions.

The activities feature CBL programs with user-friendly, on-screen menus and procedures to aid students, especially those with limited knowledge of the TI-82 or CBL. Each program has an option for retrieving and viewing sample data sets. This is particularly useful for times when a particular sensor or probe is not available or the collection of new data is not possible. Diskettes are included—for both Macintosh and MS-DOS computers—from which activity programs and sample data may be downloaded. A "share" program enables students to link calculators and transfer collected or sample data for individual analysis.

Many people helped us create this workbook. Ed Cho, The Kiski School, Class of 1995, prepared the original artwork, which was enhanced by Jay Garrison Studio. Our Texas Instruments liaisons, Scott Webb and Guy Harris, were instrumental in coordinating this project and dedicated much time and energy to making it possible. As well, we would like to thank David and Christine Vernier, Rick Sorenson, and Dan Holmquist, of Vernier Software, for their helpful comments and suggestions at the beginning of this endeavor. A special thanks to the many students and teachers at our schools for their willingness to test these activities in their classrooms and provide us with useful feedback. And finally, thanks to Sallie Huffman whose tireless editorial efforts improved the quality of this workbook significantly.

Chris Brueningsen

Bill Bower

Linda Antinone

Elisa Brueningsen

June, 1995

LOADING CBL PROGRAMS AND SAMPLE DATA ONTO YOUR TI-82

The TI-82 programs used in *Real-World Math with the CBL™ System* are available on both Macintosh and IBM-compatible diskettes located at the back of the workbook. Included on these diskettes are activity group files containing the CBL program(s) required to do each activity, together with a program containing lists of sample data for the activity. Each group file is identified by its workbook activity number.

The following three sections provide directions for using TI-GRAPH LINK software to download these files to your TI-82 calculator from a computer.

FOR MACINTOSH COMPUTERS:

1. Insert the workbook diskette into the computer disk drive. Start the TI-GRAPH LINK software on the Macintosh.

2. Connect your TI-82 and your computer with the gray TI-GRAPH LINK cable.

3. On your TI-82, press 2nd [LINK] ▶ ENTER to put the calculator in RECEIVE mode. The TI-82 displays the message **Waiting....**

4. On the Macintosh, open the Send menu and choose **Group**.

5. Click on **Desktop** and select **CBL W/B3**. Use ↑ and ↓ to move among the activity group file names.

6. Click on **Open** for the file you want to send to the TI-82.

    Note: You can send only one group file at a time.

7. Click on **SEND** to transmit the file. If you receive a "Memory Full" error on your TI-82, delete some items from your calculator and re-start the downloading process.

8. The TI-82 displays the name of each item as it is received. If the name of a file you send matches the name of an existing item, the **Duplicate Name** menu is displayed on the TI-82. You may do one of the following:

    *   Overwrite the existing item.
    *   Rename the incoming item.
    *   Omit (skip to) the next item.
    *   Quit (exit) without sending any more items.

9. After the file has been sent, the software returns to the LINK desktop.

FOR IBM-COMPATIBLE COMPUTERS WITH MS-DOS:

1. Insert the workbook diskette into the computer disk drive. Start the TI-GRAPH LINK software on your PC.

2. Connect your TI-82 and your computer with the gray TI-GRAPH LINK cable.

3. On your TI-82, press [2nd] [LINK] [▶] [ENTER] to put the calculator in RECEIVE mode. The TI-82 displays the message **Waiting....**

4. On the PC, press **U** to access the Utilities menu; press **S** to open the System Setup screen; and press **P** to modify the directory pathname. Specify **a:** as the directory pathname where the activity group files are located. (If the workbook diskette is in a different drive, substitute the correct drive letter.)

5. Press **Esc** to return to the main menu.

6. Press **S** to open the Send menu on the PC. Then press **G** for **Group**.

7. Press ↑ and ↓ to move among the activity group file names. Press **S** to mark the file(s) you want to send to the TI-82. The marked file is indicated by a square dot next to the file name.

8. When you have marked the file you want to send, press **X** to transmit the file. If you receive a "Memory Full" error on your TI-82, delete some items from your calculator and re-start the downloading process.

9. The TI-82 displays the name of each item as it is received. If the name of a file you send matches the name of an existing item, the Duplicate Name menu is displayed on the TI-82. You may do one of the following:

   - Overwrite the existing item.
   - Rename the incoming item.
   - Omit (skip to) the next item.
   - Quit (exit) without sending any more items.

10. When you are finished sending the file, press **Esc** twice to return to the main menu.

LOADING CBL PROGRAMS AND SAMPLE DATA
ONTO YOUR TI-82 (Continued)

FOR IBM-COMPATIBLE COMPUTERS WITH WINDOWS:

1. Insert the workbook diskette into the computer disk drive. Start the TI-GRAPH LINK software on your PC.

2. Connect your TI-82 and your computer with the gray TI-GRAPH LINK cable.

3. On your TI-82, press [2nd] [LINK] [▶] [ENTER] to put the calculator in RECEIVE mode. The TI-82 displays the message **Waiting....**

4. On the PC, open the Link menu, then open the Send window. Specify **a:** as the directory in which the activity group files are located. (If the workbook diskette is in a different drive, substitute the correct drive letter.)

5. Press ↑ and ↓ to move among the activity group file names. Click on the file(s) you want to send to the TI-82.

6. When you have selected the file you want to send, click on **OK** to transmit the file. If you receive a "Memory Full" error on your TI-82, delete some items from your calculator and re-start the downloading process.

7. The TI-82 displays the name of each item as it is received. If the name of a file you send matches the name of an existing item, the Duplicate Name menu is displayed on the TI-82. You may do one of the following:

    *   Overwrite the existing item.
    *   Rename the incoming item.
    *   Omit (skip to) the next item.
    *   Quit (exit) without sending any more items.

8. After the file has been sent, the application returns to the TI-GRAPH LINK desktop.

DATA TRANSFER

The activities in this workbook have been designed to afford students easy, flexible ways to collect data and share it with their classmates. Some options for transferring both newly collected data and sample data sets are summarized in the following sections.

USING SAMPLE DATA

The workbook diskette includes grouped program files for each activity in the workbook. The files are identified by activity number. For example, if you wish to perform Activity 12, download the group file entitled, "act12.82g" from the diskette. See *Loading CBL Programs and Sample Data onto Your TI-82*, page 6 for details. Because many of these programs are quite large, it will not be possible to load all of them onto your calculator at once. Also, some additional memory is required for program execution.

Each group file on the diskette contains activity program(s) and a sample data set. To access the sample data set, run the activity program and select **Use Sample** from the Options menu. A plot of the sample data will appear on your calculator screen, or instructions will tell you how to proceed. The sample data on the workbook diskette are the same sets used to answer the activity questions on the Teacher Information sheets.

The data programs are identified by activity number. For example, the data program for Activity 12 is named DATA12. If you wish to prevent someone from using a set of sample data, delete that data program from the calculator memory.

SHARING DATA WITH OTHER CALCULATORS

The workbook diskette contains a utility program called SHARE, which is used to transfer data from one calculator to another. To access this program, download the group file, "share.82g" from the workbook diskette. See *Loading CBL Programs and Sample Data onto Your TI-82*, page 6, for details.

After data has been collected or downloaded and displayed on the calculator as a statistical plot, it is possible to use SHARE to transfer both the data set and the screen image from one calculator (the "sending" calculator) to another (the "receiving" calculator). To do this, run SHARE *on the receiving calculator only*. Follow the on-screen directions to complete the data and plot-image transfer. Remember, the sending calculator does *not* run SHARE; the sending calculator only needs to be turned on for SHARE to work.

This data transfer process can be repeated from one calculator to another, provided that each receiving calculator has the SHARE program loaded onto it. Sometimes it may be convenient to collect a single set of data as a group activity, then transfer the data to everyone in the group using SHARE.

Name _____   **Date** _____

FROM HERE TO THERE   Activity 1

Many problems in applied mathematics involve finding the distance between points. If we know the coordinates of a pair of points, (x_1, y_1) and (x_2, y_2), it is easy to find the distance between them by using the following formula:

$$d = \sqrt{(x_2 - x_1)^2 + (y_2 - y_1)^2}$$

The expression above is known as the *distance formula*. It is derived directly from the Pythagorean Theorem.

In this activity you will use a pair of CBL units, each equipped with a motion detector. The motion detectors will record the coordinates of an object moving in the Cartesian plane. The data collected by the detectors will be used to experimentally verify the distance formula.

YOU NEED:

>   2 CBL Units
>   2 TI-82 Calculators with Unit-to-Unit Link Cable
>   2 Vernier CBL Motion Detectors
>   1 Dowel Rod, about 1/4" thick
>   1 Meter Stick
>   Tape

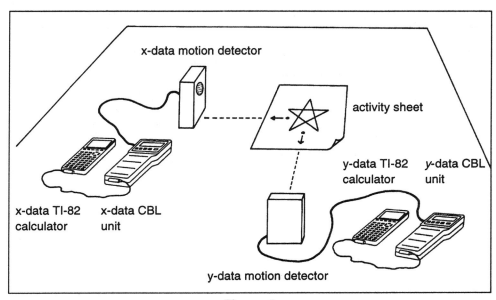

Figure 1

INSTRUCTIONS:

In this activity, the motion of a dowel rod tracing out a certain pattern will be recorded by a pair of motion detectors. It is very important to hold the rod vertically, not tilted to one side or the other. The detectors must be carefully arranged so that nothing obstructs the path between each detector and the dowel rod.

1. Remove page 15 from your workbook. It is a pattern sheet of a star with the vertices labeled with letters.

2. Tape the pattern sheet to the table. (You will trace over the pattern with the dowel rod in the course of this exercise.)

3. Set up the calculators and motion detectors as shown in Figure 1 on the previous page. Make careful note of which calculator will collect x-data and which will collect y-data.

4. After the motion detectors have been activated, you will have approximately 10 seconds to trace the pattern.

5. Start the DISTFORM program on each of your TI-82 calculators.

6. Follow the instructions on the TI-82 screen to complete the activity.

ACTIVITY DATA:

The plot that appears on the TI-82 screen should look like the star on the pattern sheet.

- If you are dissatisfied with your results, press [CLEAR] [ENTER] to start again.

- If you are satisfied with your results, press [TRACE] to move the cursor along the plot line. Identify the coordinates of each of the points labeled on the pattern sheet and write them in the table below. Give all coordinates in centimeters, rounding to the nearest tenth of a centimeter.

Point	x-coordinate	y-coordinate
A		
B		
C		
D		
E		

Sketch a picture of your star in the space provided in Figure 2.

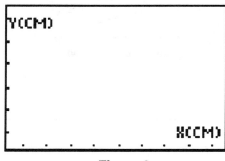

Figure 2

Name _____

QUESTIONS:

1. Notice that the star on the pattern sheet is composed of a number of line segments. Since you know the coordinates of each vertex, you should be able to find the length of any segment using the distance formula. These lengths can be verified by direct measurement with a meter stick.

    - Use the table in the Activity Data section, together with the distance formula given earlier, to find the length of each of the line segments listed in the table below. Record these measurements in the second column of the table.

    - Then use a meter stick to measure the length of each segment of the star on the pattern sheet. Round this measurement to the nearest tenth of a centimeter and record it in the last column of the table below.

Segment	Length found using distance formula	Length found by measurement
AB		
BC		
CD		
DE		
EA		

2. How do the segment lengths calculated using the distance formula compare with those found by direct measurement? Which method do you think is more accurate? Why?

    _____

    _____

3. What is the length of the total path traced out by the dowel rod? Record this value below.

    Total path length = _____

4. What is the physical interpretation of the x-coordinates in your data set?

    _____

    _____

5. What is the physical interpretation of the y-coordinates in your data set?

    _____

    _____

6. Measure the distance from the y-calculator detector to point A on the star. Round your measurement to the nearest tenth of a centimeter and record it in the space below.

Distance to point A = _____

How does this value compare with the y-coordinate of point A recorded earlier? Is this consistent with the physical interpretation in question 5?

_____

_____

EXTENSION:

A calculator program can be written to simplify the process of calculating the distance between two points. Enter the program DISTANCE, shown in Figure 3, into the TI-82 calculator. Use this program to verify the distances computed in question 1.

Figure 3

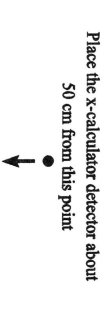

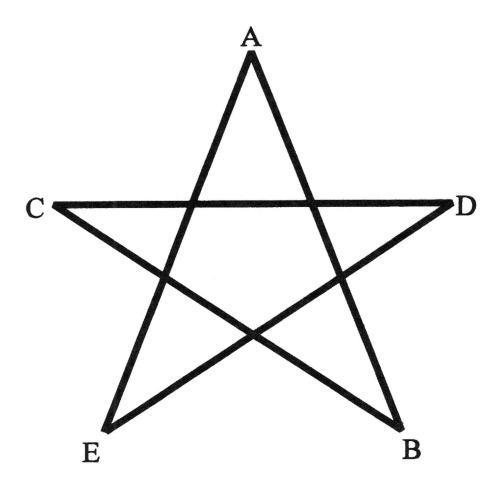

Place the y-calculator detector about
50 cm from this point

Name _____   **Date** _____

MAKING CENTS OF MATH   Activity 2

The slope of a line is generally associated with such ideas as steepness and direction. The numerical value of the slope can represent a number of other important mathematical concepts. Given any two points on a line, (x_1, y_1) and (x_2, y_2), the slope of that line can be computed using the following formula:

$$m = \frac{y_2 - y_1}{x_2 - x_1}$$

where m represents the slope of the line, x_1 and x_2 represent the *independent variable* coordinates, and y_1 and y_2 represent the *dependent variable* coordinates.

In this activity we will use the CBL and a force probe to collect a set of data points which is linear in nature. We will analyze this data and attempt to interpret the meaning of the slope as it relates to the independent and dependent variables. We will then fit a model to our data and use the model to predict future outcomes and interpret past results.

YOU NEED:

        1 CBL Unit
        1 TI-82 Calculator with Unit-to-Unit Link Cable
        1 Vernier Student Force Sensor with CBL-DIN Adapter
        1 Styrofoam Coffee Cup
        String
        32 Post-1982 Pennies

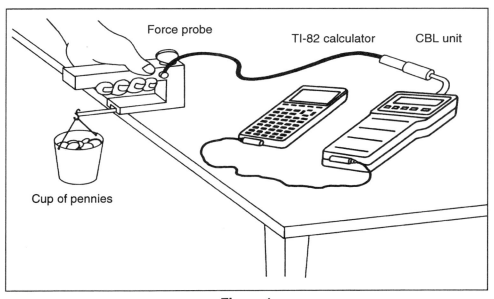

Figure 1

INSTRUCTIONS:

During this activity the CBL and force probe will be used to determine the mass of the pennies that will be placed in the bucket. Note that the force probe must be positioned as shown in the setup diagram and should remain level at all times.

1. Use a pencil to poke small holes on opposite sides of the coffee cup near the top rim. Thread a piece of string through the holes, then tie the ends of the string together to create a small bucket.

2. Suspend the bucket from the S-hook on the end of the force probe, as shown in Figure 1 on the previous page.

3. Separate your pennies into four stacks of eight pennies each. (Be sure that all 32 pennies are dated after 1982.)

4. Start the PENNIES program on your TI-82 calculator.

5. Follow the instructions on the TI-82 screen to complete the activity.

ACTIVITY DATA:

The mass vs. pennies plot should appear to be linear.

- If you are dissatisfied with your results, press [CLEAR] [ENTER] to start again.

- If you are satisfied with your results, make a rough sketch of the mass vs. number of pennies data you collected on the axes in Figure 2.

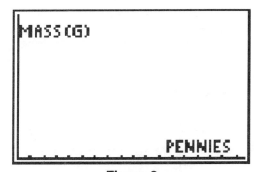

Figure 2

Press [TRACE] to move the cursor along the data points, and record the values in the table below, rounding to the nearest whole gram:

Number of pennies	Total mass in grams
0	0
8	
16	
24	
32	

Name _____

QUESTIONS:

1. The slope of a line can be defined as the ratio of the change in a pair of y-values to the change in their corresponding x-values.

   Find the slope of the line passing through any two points in your table and record it in the space below:

   $$m = \underline{\hspace{2cm}}$$

2. What do the x-values in this problem represent?

   _____

   _____

3. What do the y-values represent?

   _____

   _____

4. If slope can be described as change in y over change in x, then from questions 2 and 3 above, in our activity, slope represents:

   Change in the_____ over the change in the_____

5 Simplifying the answer to question 4, we can determine that the value for slope in this data set represents:

   The _____ per _____

6. The slope-intercept form of a line is $y = mx + b$ where m represents the slope and b is the y-intercept. The y-intercept is the y value when $x = 0$. Determine this value from the table and record it below:

   y-intercept: $b =$ _____

   Use the values for m and b found above to write the equation of the line through your data:

   _____

   _____

7. On the TI-82, press ⃞Y= and use the arrow keys to move to the first available function register. Enter the equation found in question 6, then press ⃞GRAPH to see the data together with this line. Does it appear to be a reasonably good fit for the data?

    _____

8. The TI-82 calculatorhas a built-in feature that allows it to compute best-fitting line through a set of data. This procedure is called a *linear regression*. To perform a linear regression on the data you have collected, press ⃞STAT ⃞▸. Select **LinReg** or press ⃞5 to place the linear regression command on the home screen. Press ⃞ENTER to execute this command. Copy the values which appear on your calculator screen into Figure 3 at the right.

    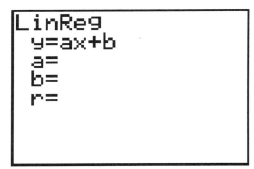

    Figure 3

    Are the values of a and b in the linear regression equation consistent with your results from question 6?

    _____

    Press ⃞Y= and use the arrow keys to move to the first unused function register. Press ⃞VARS ⃞5 ⃞▸ ⃞▸ ⃞7 to copy the regression equation the Y= list. Press ⃞GRAPH to display the data, the line from question 6, and the regression line found above all on the same screen.

9. How would using quarters affect the slope of the graph?

    _____

    _____

10. What would the slope of a graph made with quarters represent?

    _____

    _____

Name _____

APPLICATIONS:

Use your model from the activity to answer the following questions:

1. Courtney has been saving her pennies for a rainy day. She has lived in the desert all of her life and, by the time the rainy day arrives, she has saved $4,763.89! What is the total mass of her pennies?

_____ grams

2. While cleaning out the attic Kelly finds an old antique milk can that contains a large number of pennies. He weighs the can of pennies and finds that it is 45 kilograms. He then empties out the can and finds that it weighs 10 kilograms alone. Use your model to find how much money Kelly has found.
   Hint: remember that 1 kilogram = 1000 grams.

$_____

EXTENSION:

The data you collected in this activity depends on the fact that your pennies were all dated after 1982. Repeat this activity with a group of pennies dated before 1982. Use the modeling procedure described in this activity to find the average mass of a pre-1982 penny. Look in a coin book and determine why the model for pre-1982 pennies differs from the model for post 1982 pennies. How do your values for the weights of pre-1982 and post-1982 pennies compare with their official weights?

Name _____ **Date** _____

POOL PLUNGE   Activity 3

If you have ever attempted to dive to the bottom of a swimming pool you may have noticed an increased level of pressure on your eardrums as you descended to the bottom. The deeper you dive, the more water there is above you to push down on your body and your eardrums, so the more pressure you experience. As you might have guessed, there is a mathematical relationship between your depth in the pool and the pressure you feel.

In this activity we will lower a section of tubing to the bottom of the swimming pool and attempt to collect pressure readings at different depths with the use of the CBL system and a pressure sensor. We will then attempt to find a model for our data and use this model to better understand the effect of depth on pressure.

YOU NEED:

1 CBL Unit
1 TI-82 Calculator with Unit-to-Unit Link Cable
1 Vernier Pressure Sensor
20-foot Piece of Plastic Tubing (aquarium air tubing from a pet store works well and is relatively inexpensive)
1 Paper Clip
A weight heavy enough to pull the tubing to the bottom of the pool (a large fishing sinker works well)
Permanent Marking Pen
Ruler
Access to a swimming pool

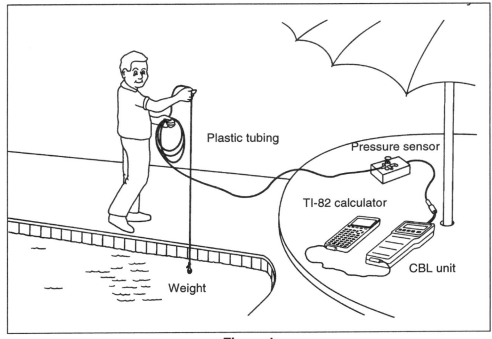

Figure 1

INSTRUCTIONS:

1. Make a small hole in one end of the plastic tubing. Attach a paper clip to the tubing through the hole. This clip will be used as a hanger for the sinker weight.

2. Beginning at the end of the tubing where the paper clip is attached, mark off intervals of one foot until you have exceeded the depth of your pool.

3. Attach the sinker weight to the paper clip.

4. Attach the other end of the plastic tubing to the pressure sensor, as shown in Figure 1.

5. Stand at the edge of the pool and get ready to lower the weighted end of the tubing into the water. When prompted by the calculator, lower the tubing into the pool one foot at a time.

6. Start the POOL program on your TI-82 calculator.

7. Follow the instructions on the TI-82 screen to complete the activity.

ACTIVITY DATA:

Your pressure vs. depth plot should appear to be linear.

-   If you are not satisfied with your data, press CLEAR ENTER and start again.

-   If you are satisfied with your data, make a rough sketch of the pressure vs. depth data that you collected on the axes in Figure 2. Be sure to show the vertical axis on your sketch.

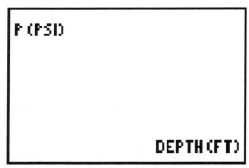

Figure 2

QUESTIONS:

1. On the TI-82, press TRACE to move the cursor along the data points. Choose any two points (X_1, Y_1) and (X_2, Y_2) along the data plot and record them in the table below. Round these values to the nearest hundredth.

X: Depth (feet)	Y: Pressure (psi)

2. Use the points in the table above to compute the slope, m, of the pressure vs. depth line and record it below:

$$m = \frac{Y_2 - Y_1}{X_2 - X_1} = \text{_____}$$

3. You will model the data with a linear equation of the form $Y = mX + B$, where B represents the y-intercept (that is, the initial pressure reading). Press TRACE and record the y-intercept value in the space below:

$$B = \text{_____}$$

Use the values of m and B determined above to write a linear equation that models your data:

_____

4. Press Y= and use the arrow keys to move to the first unused function register. Enter the equation found in question 3, then press GRAPH to see the data together with this line. Does it appear to provide a good fit for the data?

_____

5. The TI-82 calculator has a built-in feature that allows it to compute best-fitting line through a set of data. This procedure is called a *linear regression*. To perform a linear regression on the data you have collected, press STAT ▶. Select **LinReg** or press 5 to copy the linear regression command to the home screen. Press ENTER to execute this command. Copy the values which appear on your calculator screen into the matching table in Figure 3.

Figure 3

How do the values of a and b in the linear regression equation compare with the m and B values found earlier?

_____

Press Y= and use the arrow keys to move to the first unused function register. Press VARS 5 ▶ ▶ 7 to copy the regression equation found above into the Y= list. Press GRAPH to display the data, the line from question 3, and the regression line on the same screen.

Name _____

APPLICATIONS:

Use the mathematical model developed in this activity to solve the following problems.

1. Your cousin Susie is always bragging about her exploits. When you tell her that you touched the bottom of your 12-foot deep pool she quickly responds that her pool is two-and-a-half times that deep, and she always touches the bottom. Use your model to find the pressure at the bottom of Susie's pool and record your answer in the space below.

   _____ psi

2. Beginning divers are advised not swim in deep waters where the pressure exceeds about 40 psi. Use your model to determine how deep a novice diver can swim safely. **Hint:** To predict depth when pressure is given, graph a horizontal line at $y = 40$, then determine where this line intersects the modeling equation.

   _____ feet

3. The Marianis Trench contains some of the deepest waters ever measured on earth. One location was found to be 36,201 feet. Use your model to predict the pressure at this depth, and record your answer in the space below.

   _____ psi

4. The wreck of the Titanic rests on the floor of the Atlantic Ocean nearly 2.5 miles beneath the surface of the water. What is the pressure on the remains of the hull at this depth? **Hint:** 1 mile is 5280 feet.

   _____ psi

Name _____ Date _____

MEET YOU AT THE INTERSECTION Activity 4

Many times, the solution to a real-life problem involves solving more than one mathematical equation at the same time. The simplest situation of this type involves a pair of equations with two unknown quantities called a *linear system*. Geometrically, the solution to this kind of system represents the point where the graphs of these two lines intersect.

For example, imagine that a person is running to catch up to his friend who is walking ahead of him. These motions can be modeled graphically by plotting distance vs. time with time on the x-axis. The motion graphs are linear if each person is moving at a constant speed. If the plots are made on the same set of axes, the point where the two lines cross represents the physical location where the two friends pass each other.

It is possible to model situations of this type in the classroom using two TI-82 calculators, each equipped with a CBL unit and a motion detector. In this activity you will collect and analyze motion data in order to determine the solution to a linear system of equations.

YOU NEED:

    2 CBL Units
    2 TI-82 Calculators with Unit-to-Unit Link Cables
    2 Vernier CBL Motion Detectors
    1 Stopwatch
    1 Meter Stick
    Masking Tape

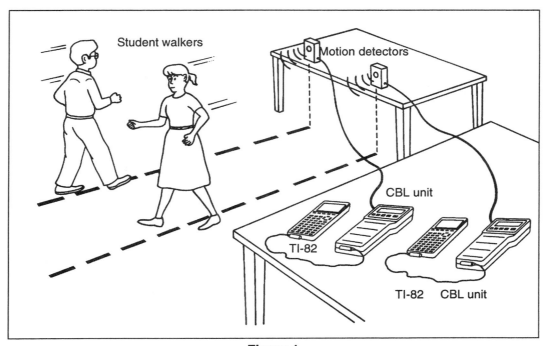

Figure 1

INSTRUCTIONS:

1. For this activity, you will use two TI-82 calculators each equipped with a CBL and a motion detector, as shown in Figure 1.

2. During this activity, one student will walk towards a motion detector while another student walks away from a second detector. These students are designated "Walker 1" and "Walker 2," respectively. When you run the activity, be sure to select "Walker 1" on one of the calculators and "Walker 2" on the other.

3. For each trial one student is responsible for starting the stopwatch when the motion detectors are activated and stopping it as soon as the students pass each other. In the CBL program, this student is called the "timer." Another student is responsible for marking the exact position on the floor where the students pass each other.

4. After the motion detectors have been activated, you will have approximately 10 seconds to collect data.

5. Start the MEETYOU program on your TI-82 calculator.

6. Follow the instructions on the TI-82 screen to complete the activity. Record the relevant data from each trial in the table below.

ACTIVITY DATA:

Where did the walkers cross paths? Measure the distance from the detectors to this location using a meter stick and record it below. Also, record the time when they crossed paths (this is the time shown on the stopwatch) rounded to the nearest tenth of a second.

Intersection Time (seconds)	Intersection Location (meters)

The combined distance-time data should show two linear plots that intersect somewhere on the TI-82 screen.

- If you need to redo your data, press CLEAR ENTER to start again.

- If you are satisfied with your results, sketch the combined data in the space provided below.

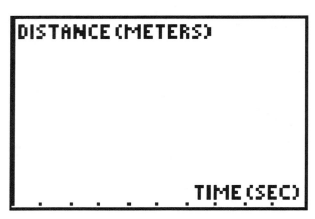

Name _____

QUESTIONS:

1. Press ⬚TRACE to position the cursor at the beginning of the plot for Walker 1. Record the *y*-intercept to the nearest hundredth in the space provided below:

    y-intercept for Walker 1: _____

    Press ⬇ to move onto the plot for Walker 2. Record the *y*-intercept for Walker 2 below:

    y-intercept for Walker 2: _____

    What is the physical meaning of these values?

    _____

2. Press ⬆ to move back onto the plot for Walker 1. Use the arrow keys to move along this plot. Identify any two points (x_1, y_1) and (x_2, y_2) and record them below:

	x_1	y_1	x_2	y_2
Walker 1				

    Press ⬇ to move to the plot for Walker 2 and repeat this procedure:

	x_1	y_1	x_2	y_2
Walker 2				

3. When the coordinates of two points on a line are known, the slope of the line can be computed by finding the difference in *y* values divided by the difference in *x* values:

    $$slope = \frac{y_2 - y_1}{x_2 - x_1}$$

    Use this formula to compute the slope for each plot. Record your answers below:

    Slope for Walker 1: _____

    Slope for Walker 2: _____

4. How is the sign (positive or negative) of each slope related to the direction the walker is moving with respect to the motion detector?

_____

_____

How is the magnitude (steepness) of the slope related to the speed of the each walker?

_____

_____

5. The slope-intercept form of a linear equation is $y = mx + b$, where m is the slope of the line and b is the y-intercept. Use the information you found above to write linear equations to model the motion of the walkers:

Equation for Walker 1: _____

Equation for Walker 2: _____

Press [Y=] and move the cursor to the first unused function location. Enter the equation for Walker 1 here. Move the cursor to the next unused function location and enter the equation for Walker 2. Press [GRAPH] to see these equations together with the data you collected. How do the equations fit the data?

_____

You may wish to adjust your slope and/or intercept values slightly if you are not satisfied with the way the lines fit the data. If you adjust these values, rewrite the equations above.

Name _____

6. Where do the two lines intersect? To find out, press [2nd] [CALC] [5] to access the intersect feature of the TI-82. Press [ENTER] to identify the first curve and [ENTER] again for the second curve. When prompted for a "Guess," use [◄] or [►] to move the cursor to a point near the intersection and press [ENTER]. The result cursor is on the solution, and the coordinate values are displayed at the bottom of the screen. Record the intersection coordinates, rounded to the nearest hundredth, below:

x-value: _____

y-value: _____

What is the physical meaning of these values? How do they compare to the intersection time and intersection location values you recorded in the Activity Data section?

_____

_____

_____

7. Would it be possible for the walkers to move in front of the motion detectors so that the resulting data plots would not intersect? If so, give an example; if not, explain why.

_____

_____

Could the walkers move in front of the detectors so that their data plots would intersect more than once? If so, how?

_____

_____

EXTENSION:

Repeat the activity. This time, have the walkers move at non-constant speeds, starting off slowly then speeding up. The resulting data plots will be non-linear. What type of function could be used to model these distance vs. time plots?

STRETCH IT TO THE LIMIT   Activity 5

When a force is applied to a rubberband, it stretches a certain amount. Exactly how much it stretches depends on the applied force and the characteristics of the rubberband. In general, the more force that is applied, the more it stretches. Two quantities, x and y, that change in this way are said to vary directly and are related by the equation:

$$y = kx$$

where k is a positive constant.

In this activity, you will use the CBL system, together with a force sensor and a motion detector, to investigate the general relationship between force applied to a rubberband and the amount that the rubberband stretches.

YOU NEED:

> 1 CBL Unit
> 1 TI-82 Calculator with Unit-to-Unit Link Cable
> 1 Vernier CBL Motion Detector
> 1 Vernier Student Force Sensor
> 1 Long Rubberband (or 3 smaller ones)

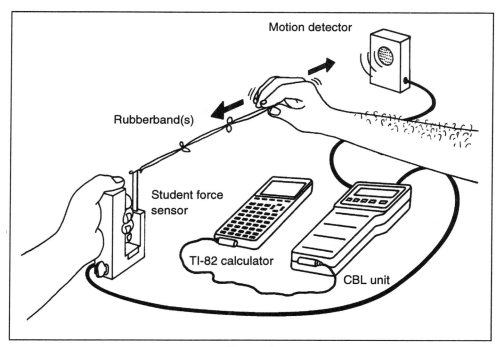

Figure 1

INSTRUCTIONS:

1. For this activity, you will flex and relax a rubberband with your hand. A motion detector will record the amount the rubberband is stretched while a force sensor measures the force of your pull. Be sure not to get closer than two feet to the detector during the data collection.

2. The rubberband being used should be flexible enough to stretch at least 6 inches. Several smaller rubberbands linked together also work well for this activity.

3. Start the STRETCH program on your TI-82 calculator.

4. Follow the instructions on the TI-82 screen to complete the activity.

ACTIVITY DATA:

The data you collected should go through the origin and appear to be linear.

Figure 2

- If you are not satisfied with your results, repeat the procedure by pressing [CLEAR] [ENTER].

- If you are satisfied with your results, make a rough sketch of the force vs. position data on the axes provided in Figure 2.

QUESTIONS:

1. As mentioned earlier, force and position vary directly when a rubberband is stretched. To test this, press [Y=] and move the cursor to the first unused function register. Enter the expression $K*X$ and then press [2nd] [QUIT] to return to the home screen. In order to arrive at a good model for the data, the constant value, K, must be determined and stored in the calculator. Begin with $K=1$ by pressing [1] [STO▸] [ALPHA] [K] [ENTER]. Then press [GRAPH] to see the data and curve on the same screen. Repeat the keystrokes in the previous sentence to store different values for K until you find one that provides a good fit for the data. In the space below, record the value of K that works best:

$$K = \underline{\hspace{2cm}}$$

2. The K-value may also be determined algebraically by substituting a value of x and its corresponding y-value into the variation equation, $y = kx$. To choose the x- and y-coordinates, press [TRACE] and move the cursor to any data point on the graph. Record the x and y values, rounded to the nearest hundredth, in the spaces below. Use these values to solve for k, and write this value in the table provided.

x	
y	
k	

Are the K values determined in questions 1 and 2 consistent? What might cause them to be slightly different?

_____

_____

3. Your predicted value of K can be tested using a built-in feature of the TI-82 that allows it to compute the best-fitting line through a set of data. This procedure is called a *linear regression*. To perform a linear regression on the data you have collected, press [STAT] and select **LinReg** or [5] to copy the command to the home screen. Then, press [ENTER] to compute the regression equation. Copy the values which appear on your calculator screen into the matching table in Figure 3.

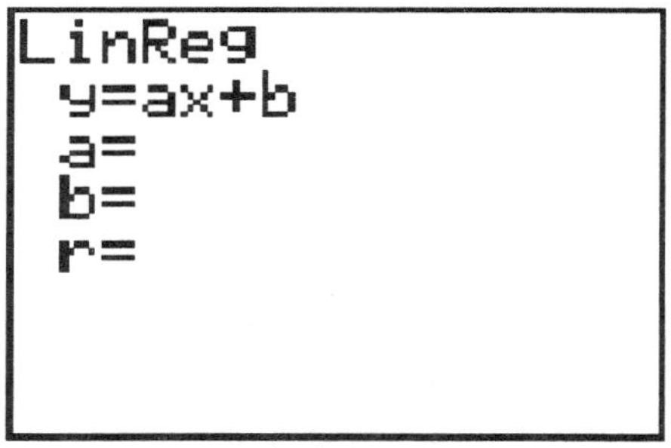

```
LinReg
 y=ax+b
 a=
 b=
 r=
```

Figure 3

How does the value of a in the linear regression compare with the K values found in questions 1 and 2?

_____

_____

What should the b value from the regression be? Explain.

_____

_____

4. In order to graph the regression equation computed above, press [Y=] and use the arrow keys to move to the first unused function register. Press [VARS] [5] [▶] [▶] [7] to copy the regression equation into the Y= list. Press [GRAPH] to see the data, the line from question 1, and the regression line found in question 3 all on the same screen.

   Which equation seems to fit better? Which equation is a better direct variation model? Why?

_____

_____

_____

5. Explain why the graph is linear even though you stretched the rubberband back and forth in front of the motion detector.

    _____

    _____

6. How would your data be affected if you used a less flexible rubberband? How would this change your K value?

    _____

    _____

EXTENSION:

As you were recording motion and force data for the stretched and relaxed rubberband, time values were being recorded simultaneously by the CBL. These values are stored in list L_3 on the calculator that was used to collect the data. Press 2nd [STAT PLOT] 4 ENTER to turn off all data plots. Make a plot of L_2 (y-data, force) vs. L_3 (x-data, time). This plot shows how force values vary with time while you were pulling on the rubberband. Make a predication about what a plot of stretch distance vs. time would look like. Check your prediction by making a second plot of L_1 (y-data, stretch distance) vs. L_3 (x-data, time). How is the stretch distance vs. time plot related to the force vs. time plot? Be specific.

UNDER PRESSURE | Activity 6

When a gas inside a closed container is compressed, its pressure and volume usually change. As the force exerted on the gas increases, the pressure increases while its volume decreases. Two quantities that change in this sort of way are said to vary *inversely*. Even though both quantities may change, their product always stays the same. Suppose that x and y represent the quantities that are inversely related. Then

$$xy = k$$

or, stated another way,

$$y = \frac{k}{x}$$

where k represents a positive constant in both equations. Maybe you can think of some other quantities that behave this way also.

In this activity, you will use the CBL system and a pressure sensor to investigate the general relationship between pressure and volume for air contained within a closed syringe.

YOU NEED:

> 1 CBL Unit
> 1 TI-82 Calculator with Unit-to-Unit Link Cable
> 1 Vernier Pressure Sensor with CBL-DIN adapter
> Syringe Attachment with the short piece of plastic tubing

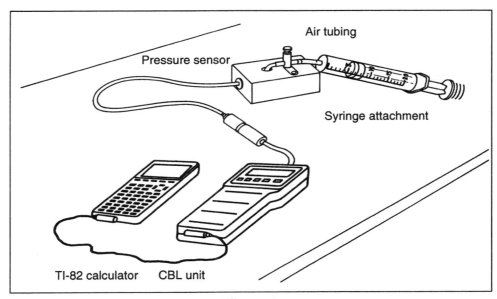

Figure 1

INSTRUCTIONS:

The pressure in the syringe will be varied during the activity by pressing on the syringe plunger.

1. Attach the syringe to the pressure sensor with the short piece of tubing as shown in Figure 1 on the previous page.

2. Start the PRESSURE program on your TI-82 calculator.

3. Follow the instructions on the TI-82 screen to complete the activity.

ACTIVITY DATA:

Your data plot should show pressure values that decrease as volume increases.

- If your results are not consistent with this trend, press CLEAR ENTER to start again.

- If your results are consistent with this trend, sketch the pressure vs. volume plot on the axes provided in Figure 2.

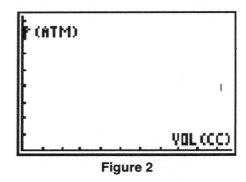

Figure 2

QUESTIONS:

1. According to scientific theory, pressure and volume vary inversely. To test this, press Y= and move the cursor to the first unused function register. Enter the expression K/X. You will need to adjust the value of K in order to obtain a good fit for the data. Try different values for K by entering a number at the home screen then pressing STO▸ ALPHA [K] ENTER. Start with $K = 1$. Press GRAPH to see the data and curve together. Continue this process until you find a K value that gives a good fit. Record the value of K that works best in the space below:

$$K = \underline{\hspace{2cm}}$$

Using your K value, complete the modeling equation and record it below:

_____

2. Press TRACE and use the ◀ and ▶ keys to move the cursor along your data plots. Record the data points from this activity in the first two columns of the table on the next page. Find the product of the data coordinates and record it in the third column of the table. Express your values to the nearest tenth of a unit.

Volume (*x*-values)	Pressure (*y*-values)	Product (*x* ∗ *y*)

Notice that the values in the third column are closely related to the value of K found in question 1. Explain why this is so.

_____

_____

3. The modeling equation you have determined in this activity can be used to predict syringe pressure values for given volumes. The table below lists a number of volumes. You need to fill in the corresponding pressures.

To do this, access the Table Setup Menu on your TI-82 calculator by pressing [2nd] [TblSet]. Move around the screen with the arrow keys and adjust the settings to match those shown in the display in Figure 3. To select **Auto** or **Ask**, simply highlight your choice and press [ENTER].

Figure 3

After the settings have been adjusted, press [2nd] [TABLE] to access the table editor. Enter the volumes as *x*-values and record the corresponding pressures in the table below.

Volume (cc) (*x*-values)	Pressure (atm) (*y*-values)
2.5	
17.8	
520	
0.0012	

4. Could the volume ever be zero cc? Why or why not?
   Hint: What would be the corresponding pressure?

   _____

   _____

5. Complete the following statement:

   As the volume of a gas decreases, its pressure _____

EXTENSION:

An alternate way to find an appropriate model for the data you collected in this activity involves a process known as *regression analysis*. To perform a power regression on the data you collected, press STAT ▶ and select **PwrReg** from this menu, or press ALPHA [B] to place the power regression command on the home screen. Press ENTER to execute the power regression. Record the resulting regression equation. Is it consistent with the model you discovered in this activity?

If you'd like to see how well this equation fits the data you collected, press Y= and use the arrow keys to move to the first unused function register. Press VARS 5 ▶ ▶ 7 to copy this regression equation into the Y= list. Press GRAPH to display the data and regression curve on the same screen.

Name _____ Date _____

LIGHT AT A DISTANCE   Activity 7

While traveling in a car at night, you've probably had an opportunity to observe the bright headlights of an oncoming vehicle. The light starts as a dim glow in the distance, but as the vehicle gets closer, the brightness of the headlights increases rapidly. This happens because light waves tend to spread out as they move away from their source. As a result, intensity decreases quickly as the distance from a light source increases. But is there an exact mathematical relationship between the distance from a light source and the intensity you observe?

In this activity you will use a light sensor along with the CBL unit to find out. You will record changes in light intensity as the sensor is moved away from a light bulb. The resulting data will be analyzed and modeled mathematically.

YOU NEED:

      1 CBL Unit
      1 TI-82 Calculator with Unit-to-Unit Link Cable
      1 TI Light Probe
      1 Light Socket
      1 Light Bulb (60 Watts or less)
      1 Meter Stick

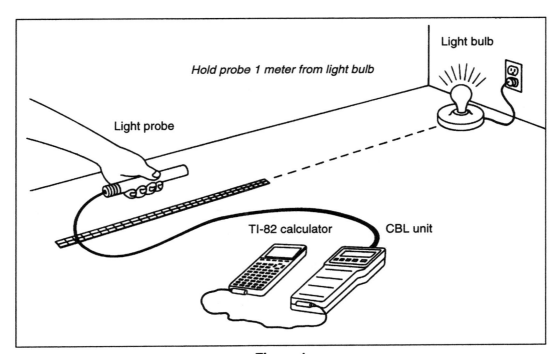

Figure 1

INSTRUCTIONS:

1. Mark off distances of one meter and two meters from the light socket. Then divide the distance into 10-centimeter intervals between the one-meter and two-meter marks.

2. While you are taking intensity readings during the activity, the light sensor should be pointed directly at the illuminated bulb with the end of the sensor held a certain distance from the bulb, as specified in the calculator program.

3. Make sure that nothing obstructs the path between the light source and the light sensor when readings are being taken. Individuals with brightly colored clothes should avoid standing near the light bulb as this may cause erroneous intensity readings due to reflected light.

4. Darken the room with the exception of the light source.

5. Start the BULB program on your TI-82 calculator.

6. Follow the instructions on the TI-82 screen to complete the activity.

ACTIVITY DATA:

Your data plot should show intensity values that decrease as distances increase.

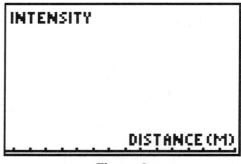

Figure 2

- If you are dissatisfied with your results, press [CLEAR] [ENTER] to start again.

- If you are satisfied with your results, sketch the light intensity vs. distance graph on the axes in Figure 2.

QUESTIONS:

1. The data you collected will be modeled with a power relation of the form $Y = A*X^B$. First, you will need to find the values of A and B.

   Consider the case where the distance from the bulb is $X = 1$ meter. Substituting into the equation above gives $Y = A*(1)^B$, or simply $Y = A$. Press [TRACE] and use the arrow keys to move the cursor to the data point where $X = 1$. Record the corresponding y-value, carried out to four decimal places, as A below.

$$A = \underline{\hspace{3cm}}$$

2. To find B, press [TRACE] and use the arrow keys to move the cursor to any data point other than the one used above. Record the X and Y coordinates of this point in the spaces below. Round these values to four decimal places.

$$X = \underline{\hspace{3cm}} \qquad Y = \underline{\hspace{3cm}}$$

   Substitute the values of A, X, and Y into the equation $Y = A*X^B$. Notice that the only unknown in the resulting equation is B. Record this equation below:

Name _____

3. Rewrite the equation in question 2 as an expression that is equal to zero. Record this equation below.

_____ $= 0$

4. Solve the expression in question 3 for B. The **solve(** feature of the TI-82 calculator makes this easy. This feature finds a solution of an expression set equal to zero, for a specified variable, when given an initial guess. The syntax for this command is :

$$\textbf{solve}(expression,\ variable,\ guess)$$

To place this command on the home screen, press MATH 0. Enter the left side of the expression you found in question 3 followed by ⌐. Enter the variable you wish to solve for by pressing ALPHA [B] followed by ⌐. Finally, enter your guess for the value of B (almost any value will do). Close the parentheses by pressing ⌐, then press ENTER to find the value of B. Record this value, rounded to the nearest hundredth, below:

$B =$ _____

5. Substitute your values for A and B into the equation $Y = A*X^\wedge B$ and record this equation in the space provided:

_____

6. Press Y= and move the cursor to the first unused function register. Enter the equation you found above and press GRAPH to see your model and the data on the same screen. How well does your model fit the data?

_____

7. How would using a brighter or dimmer light bulb affect the values of A and B, if at all?

_____

_____

8. The TI-82 calculator has a built-in feature that allows it to compute the best-fitting curves for different data sets. This process is called *regression analysis*. In this case, you will perform a power regression on the data you collected. To do this, press ⸢STAT⸥ ⸢▶⸥ and select **PwrReg** or ⸢ALPHA⸥ [B] to copy the command to the home screen. Press ⸢ENTER⸥ and copy the values which appear on your calculator screen into the matching table in Figure 3.

   Are the values of a and b in the power regression equation consistent with the values of A and B you found earlier?

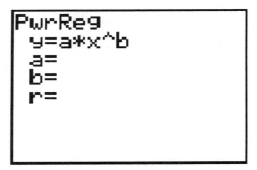

Figure 3

_____

Press ⸢Y=⸥ and use the arrow keys to move the cursor to the next unused function location. Press ⸢VARS⸥ ⸢5⸥ ⸢▶⸥ ⸢▶⸥ ⸢7⸥ to copy the regression equation into the Y= list. Press ⸢GRAPH⸥ to see the data, the curve from question 6, and the regression curve found above on the same screen.

9. According to scientific theory, the correct model for light intensity vs. distance is an inverse square relationship. This relation is expressed mathematically as:

$$Y = \frac{A}{X^2}$$

   If this equation is expressed in the form $Y = A*X^\wedge B$, what would be the value of B? Is this consistent with the models you found earlier?

_____

_____

APPLICATIONS:

1. Suppose that your patio is illuminated by an overhead light source with two bulbs. You decide to save on electricity by removing one of the bulbs. If the light is currently mounted 5 meters off the ground, at what height should it be moved to in order to retain the same amount of light on your patio with one bulb?

2. Two identical light bulbs shine on your favorite reading chair from different locations in the room. The first bulb is 3 meters from your chair and provides an intensity of 0.6 mW/cm². The second is 2 meters from your chair. What intensity does this bulb provide?

WHAT GOES UP...   Activity 8

Naturally, when a cart or a ball is given a push up a ramp, it will roll back down again after reaching its highest point. Algebraically, the relationship between the distance and elapsed time for the cart is quadratic in the general form:

$$y = ax^2 + bx + c$$

where y represents the distance the ball has traveled up the ramp and x represents the elapsed time. The quantities a, b, and c are constants which depend on the such things as the inclination angle of the ramp and the cart's initial speed. Although the cart moves back and forth in a straight-line path, a plot of its distance along the ramp graphed as a function of time is parabolic.

Generally, parabolas have several important points including the vertex (the maximum or minimum point), the y-intercept (where the graph crosses the y-axis), and the x-intercepts (where the graph crosses the x-axis). The x- and y-intercepts are actually related to the constants a, b, and c given in the equation above according to the following properties:

---

1. The y-intercept is equal to the constant c.

2. The product of the x-intercepts is equal to $\dfrac{c}{a}$.

3. The sum of the x-intercepts is equal to $-\dfrac{b}{a}$.

Box 1

So, if you know the x- and y-intercepts of a parabola, you can find its general form equation.

In this activity, a motion detector will be connected to a CBL system and used to measure how the distance of a cart on a ramp changes with time. The motion plot of the cart will be analyzed and its parabolic features will be considered.

YOU NEED:

> 1 CBL Unit
> 1 TI-82 Calculator with Unit-to-Unit Link Cable
> 1 Vernier CBL Motion Detector
> 1 Four-Wheel Cart (a ball can be substituted)
> Flat Wooden Board, about 8 feet long and 1 foot wide
> Several Books to support the end of the ramp

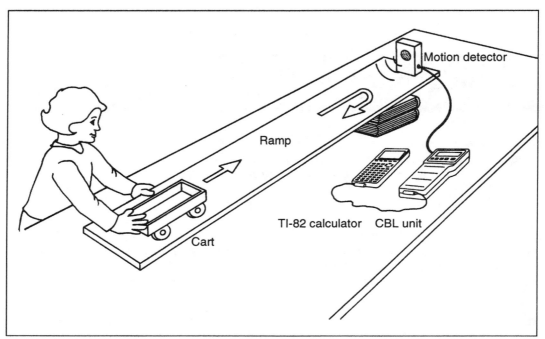

Figure 1

INSTRUCTIONS:

When the cart is given a push up the ramp, it should slowly come to rest as it reaches its highest point, then return to its starting point. The entire process should take several seconds.

1. Place one or two books beneath one end of the board to make an inclined ramp. The inclination angle should only be a few degrees.

2. Be sure to place the motion detector at the top of the ramp as shown in Figure 1 above. Note that you will be pushing the cart *towards* the detector during the activity. *At no time should the cart come closer than 2 feet from the detector during the exercise.*

3. The cart must pass the position at which it is zeroed both on its way up and on its way back down the ramp while data is being collected.

4. Start the RAMP program on your TI-82 calculator.

5. Follow the instructions on the TI-82 screen to complete the activity.

ACTIVITY DATA:

The resulting plot of distance vs. time should appear to be parabolic.

*   If you are dissatisfied with your results, press CLEAR ENTER to start again. If your plot does not cross the *x*-axis twice, you need to collect a new set of data.

*   If you are satisfied with your results, make a rough sketch of the distance vs. time data you collected in the space in Figure 2. Since the axis orientation varies from trial to trial, you will need to draw in the axes on your plot sketch.

Figure 2

Name _____

QUESTIONS:

1. On the TI-82, press $\boxed{\text{TRACE}}$. Move the cursor along your distance vs. time plot and identify, to the nearest tenth of a unit, the x- and y-intercepts. Record these values in the table below.

y-intercept	First x-intercept	Second x-intercept

2. Determine the product and sum of the x-intercepts and record these values in the table below:

Product of x-intercepts	
Sum of x-intercepts	

3. Use the information from questions 1 and 2, together with the three intercept properties shown in Box 1, to determine the values of a, b, and c for the general form parabolic expression $y = ax^2 + bx + c$. Record these values in the following table.

a	
b	
c	

Hint: Write an equation for each of the three properties shown in Box 1; then solve this system of equations for a, b, and c.

Substitute the values of a, b, and c you just found into the equation $y = ax^2 + bx + c$. Record the completed modeling equation below:

_____

4. Press $\boxed{\text{Y=}}$ and move the cursor to the first unused function register. Enter the modeling equation from question 3, and press $\boxed{\text{GRAPH}}$ to display the data and curve on the same screen. How well does the curve fit the data?

_____

_____

5. The TI-82 calculator has a built-in feature that allows it to compute the best-fitting quadratic equation for a given data set. This procedure is called a *quadratic regression*. To perform a quadratic regression on the data you have collected, press [STAT] [▷]. Select **QuadReg** or press [6] to place the quadratic regression command on the home screen. Press [ENTER] to execute this command. Copy the values which appear on your calculator screen into the matching table in Figure 3.

```
QuadReg
 y=ax²+bx+c
 a=
 b=
 c=
```

Figure 3

Are the values of *a*, *b*, and *c* in the quadratic regression equation above consistent with your results from question 3?

_____

_____

Press [Y=] and use the arrow keys to move to the first unused function register. Press [VARS] [5] [▷] [▷] [7] to copy the regression equation found in part 5 into the Y= list. Press [GRAPH] to display the data, the modeling equation, and the regression curve all on the same screen.

6. In the experiment you just conducted, the vertex on the parabolic distance vs. time plot corresponds to a minimum on the graph even though this is the position at which the cart reaches its maximum distance from the starting point along the ramp. Explain why this is so.

_____

_____

7. Suppose that the experiment is repeated, but this time the motion detector is placed at the bottom of the ramp instead of at the top. Make a rough sketch of your predicted distance vs. time plot for this situation in Figure 4. Discuss how the coefficient, *a*, would be affected, if at all.

_____

_____

_____

```
DIST(FT)




                                    TIME(SEC)
```

Figure 4

THAT'S THE WAY THE BALL BOUNCES   Activity 9

As a ball bounces up and down, the maximum height it reaches continually decreases from one bounce to the next. For any particular bounce, if the ball's height is plotted as a function of time, the resulting graph has a parabolic shape. The relationship between height and time for a single bounce of a ball, then, is quadratic. This relationship is expressed mathematically as:

$$y = ax^2 + bx + c$$

where y represents the ball's height at any given time, x. It is possible to mathematically model a ball's bouncing behavior using a series of quadratic functions.

In this activity, you will record the motion of a bouncing ball using a sonic motion detector and the CBL System. You will then analyze the collected data and attempt to model the variations in a bouncing ball's height as a function of time for one particular bounce.

YOU NEED:

> 1 CBL Unit
> 1 TI-82 Calculator with Unit-to-Unit Link Cable
> 1 Vernier CBL Motion Detector
> 1 Ball (racquetballs and basketballs work well)

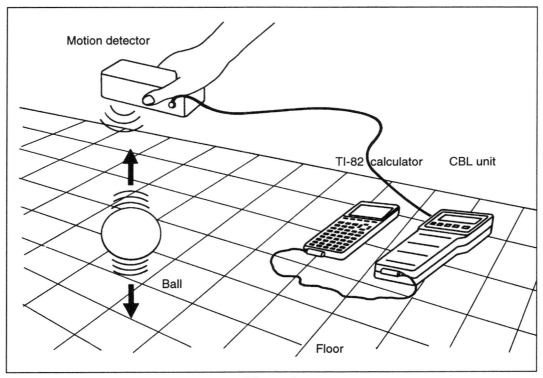

Figure 1

INSTRUCTIONS:

Be sure that the ball is bounced on a smooth, level surface. Do not allow anything to obstruct the path between the motion detector and the ball while the data is being collected.

1. Hold the motion detector about 5 or 6 feet above the floor, parallel to it, as shown in Figure 1.

2. Start the BALL program on your TI-82 calculator.

3. Follow the instructions on the TI-82 screen to complete the activity.

ACTIVITY DATA:

The resulting plot of distance vs. time should appear to be a series of parabolic sections with decreasing maximum heights.

- If you are dissatisfied with your results, press CLEAR ENTER to start again.

- If you are satisfied with your results, make a rough sketch of the distance vs. time data you collected in the space in Figure 2.

Figure 2

SELECTING THE DATA:

Run the CHOOSE program on your TI-82 calculator.

Following the on-screen instructions, select a single parabolic section from the data you have collected. You will have several parabolas to choose from, each one representing a different bounce; you only need to pick one.

The CHOOSE program stores selected heights to list L_4 and corresponding selected times to list L_3.

- If you are dissatisfied with the parabolic section you have chosen, press CLEAR ENTER and run the CHOOSE program again.

- If you are satisfied with the parabolic section you have chosen, sketch it in the space in Figure 3.

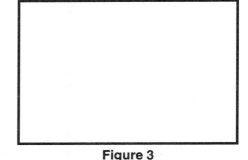

Figure 3

Real-World Math with the CBL™ System ⚡

Name _____

QUESTIONS:

1. In this activity, the ball bounced straight up and down beneath the detector, yet the plot in Figure 2 seems to depict a ball that is bouncing sideways. Explain why this is so.

   _____

   _____

2. On the TI-82, press [TRACE]. Move the cursor along your distance vs. time plot and estimate the *x*- and *y*-coordinates of the vertex of the parabola (in this case, the maximum point on the curve). Round these values to the nearest hundredth, and record them in the table below:

Vertex	
x-coordinate	*y*-coordinate

3. The theoretical model for the distance vs. time data is quadratic. We will attempt to fit our data with a quadratic function of the form:

$$y = a(x - h)^2 + k$$

   where *h* is the *x*-coordinate of the vertex, *k* is the *y*-coordinate of the vertex, and *a* is a constant. This model is called *vertex form* of a parabolic expression.

   Press [Y=] and move the cursor to the first unused function register. Enter the expression $A(X - H)^2 + K$ and then press [2nd] [QUIT] to return to the home screen. Enter the value of *H* (the *x*-coordinate of the vertex) found in question 2 above, then press [STO▸] [ALPHA] [H] [ENTER] to store this value to variable *H* on your calculator. Repeat this procedure and store the *y*-coordinate to the variable *K*.

   To obtain a good fit, you will need to adjust the value of *A*. Use the method described above to store different numbers to the variable *A*. Start with *A* = 1. Press [GRAPH] to display the data and curve on the same screen. Try different values of *A*. For each new value of *A* that you test, press [GRAPH] to view your adjusted model. Experiment until you find one that provides a good fit for the data. *Remember to test both positive and negative values for A.* Record the *A* value that works best in the space below:

   $$A = \underline{\hspace{2cm}}$$

   Using this *A* value and the values of *H* and *K* determined in question 2, complete the vertex form of the equation and record it below:

   _____

4. It is also possible to express any quadratic function in the *general form*, as described earlier:

$$y = ax^2 + bx + c$$

where the coefficient a is identical to that found in question 3 above, and b and c are other constants. To determine these coefficients, expand the equation you wrote in question 3, and collect like terms. Record the corresponding values of a, b, and c in the table below:

a	
b	
c	

5. The TI-82 calculator has a built-in feature that allows it to compute the best-fitting quadratic equation through a set of data. This procedure is called a *quadratic regression*. To perform a quadratic regression on the data you have collected, press STAT ▶. Select **QuadReg** or press 6 to place the quadratic regression command on the home screen. Then press 2nd [L₃] , 2nd [L₄] ENTER to execute the regression command on the data in lists L_3 and L_4. Copy the values which appear on your calculator screen into the matching table in Figure 4 at the right.

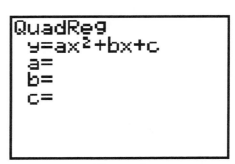

Figure 4

Are the values of a, b, and c in the quadratic regression equation above consistent with the values in your table in question 4?

_____

Press Y= and use the arrow keys to move the cursor to the first available function register. Press VARS 5 ▶ ▶ 7 to copy the regression equation found above into the Y= list. Then press GRAPH to display the data, the vertex form of the equation from question 3, and the regression curve on the same screen.

6. In your own words, describe how the constant a affects the graph of $y = a(x - h)^2 + k$. Specifically, how do the magnitude of a and the sign of a change the graph?

_____

_____

_____

7. Suppose you had chosen the parabolic section for the bounce just to the right of the one you actually used in this activity. Describe how the constants h and k would change, if at all, if this parabolic section was fit with the equation $y = a(x - h)^2 + k$.

_____

_____

_____

CALCULUS EXTENSION:

How does the value of a vary from one parabolic section to the next? Run the CHOOSE program again. This time, select any other bounce and model it as described in this activity. Explain why the values of a are in close agreement for both bounces.

Hint: Take the second derivative of the modeling equation. What is the physical significance of this value?

CHILL OUT   Activity 10

When you have a drink which is very hot you have probably noticed that it quickly cools off to a temperature that you consider tolerable. Your drink then remains in a drinkable temperature range for quite a while until it eventually cools off too much as it approaches room temperature. Newton's law of cooling provides us with a theoretical model for this situation. It states that the temperature difference between a hot object and its surroundings decreases exponentially with time.

In this activity we will use the CBL and a temperature probe to collect data which will allow us to simulate the temperature variations that occur as a liquid is cooling. We will then use the TI-82 calculator to fit a mathematical model to the data.

YOU NEED:

> 1 CBL Unit
> 1 TI-82 Calculator with Unit-to-Unit Link Cable
> 1 TI Temperature Probe
> A Cup of Hot Water

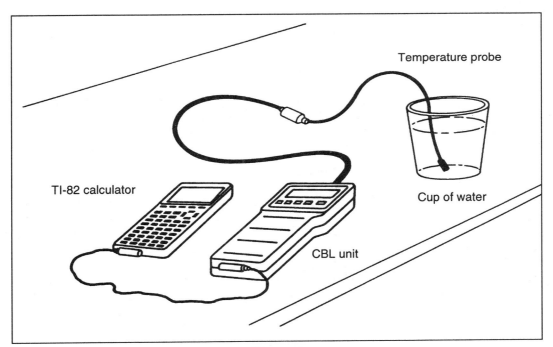

Figure 1

INSTRUCTIONS:

In this activity, we will observe temperature variations as the heated temperature probe is allowed to cool in the air. This will effectively simulate the action of a cooling cup of liquid while allowing us to collect the data in a relatively short period of time.

1. Get a cup of hot water to be used in this experiment. The water should be very hot, although it does not need to be boiling.

2. Start the CHILL program on your TI-82 calculator.

3. Follow the instructions on the TI-82 screen to complete the activity.

ACTIVITY DATA:

Your data should show temperature values that decrease rapidly at first, then level off as the time values increase.

- If your data is not satisfactory, press [CLEAR] [ENTER] to do another trial.

- If your data is satisfactory, sketch a plot of your temperature vs. time data on the axes in Figure 2.

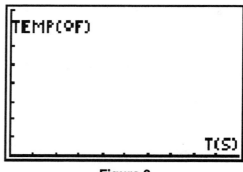

Figure 2

QUESTIONS:

1. The theoretical model for the cooling curve is exponential. We will attempt to fit our data with a curve of the form:

$$y = A B^x + C$$

where x is time and y is temperature. In this model, C represents room temperature, the value the modeling function is approaching as the curve flattens out. To obtain room temperature, read it from a wall thermostat or thermometer and record the value below.

Room temperature = _____

Press [GRAPH], then press [2nd] [DRAW] [3] to put a horizontal marker on the screen. Use the arrow keys to move this marker up and down on the screen. Make sure that your data points are all higher than the room temperature that you recorded above. The value of C must be lower than all other values on the graph because when the graph is shifted down by C units, it cannot have any negative values. If your measured room temperature is lower than all of the graph values, record it as C in the blank below. If not, record a value one or two pixel values below the lowest temperature on the graph.

$C = $ _____

2. The variable x represents time in our equation $y = A B^x + C$. Substituting $x = 0$ to find our initial temperature, we arrive at $y = A + C$. Therefore, A equals the y-intercept minus C. Press [TRACE] to identify this initial value and record it to the nearest hundredth in the space below. Solve the equation for A, and record this value in the space provided:

y-intercept = _____ $A = $ _____

---

3. Press $\boxed{Y=}$ and move the cursor to the first unused function register. Enter the expression $A*B\wedge X + C$ and then press $\boxed{2nd}$ [QUIT] to return to the home screen. Enter the value of A found above then press $\boxed{STO\blacktriangleright}$ $\boxed{ALPHA}$ [A] $\boxed{ENTER}$ to store this value to variable A on your calculator. Repeat this procedure to store variables C and B, starting with $B = 1$. Then press $\boxed{GRAPH}$ to display the data and curve on the same screen.

   To obtain a good fit, you will need to adjust the value of B. Use the method described above to store different numbers for the variable B. View the graph for each new value of B that you test. Experiment until you find a value that provides a good fit for the data. Record the B value that works best in the space below:

$$B = \underline{\hspace{3cm}}$$

4. We can also fit this curve using an *exponential regression* on the TI-82 with a few modifications. The TI-82 uses the exponential model $y = a*b\wedge x$ to fit the data. This model assumes that the curve approaches the line $y = 0$ as time values get larger and larger. In other words, the calculator assumes that $C = 0$. We can still use this model simply by applying a vertical shift of C units to our data. To achieve this, press $\boxed{STAT}$ $\boxed{ENTER}$ go to the list editor. Use the arrow keys to move to the very top of list L_3 so that L_3 is highlighted. Press $\boxed{2nd}$ [L_2] $\boxed{-}$ $\boxed{ALPHA}$ [C] $\boxed{ENTER}$.

```
ExpReg
 y=a*b^x
 a=
 b=
 r=
```
Figure 3

   What do the numbers in L_3 represent? _____

   _____

   To perform an exponential regression on the data in lists L_1 and L_3, press $\boxed{STAT}$ $\boxed{\blacktriangleright}$. Select ExpReg or press $\boxed{ALPHA}$ [A] to place the exponential regression command on the home screen. Press $\boxed{2nd}$ [L_1] $\boxed{,}$ $\boxed{2nd}$ [L_3] $\boxed{ENTER}$ to give the lists on which the regression will be calculated. Copy the values which appear on your calculator screen into Figure 3 above.

   Are the values of a and b in the exponential regression equation consistent with your results from the previous questions?

   _____

   _____

5. Press $\boxed{Y=}$ and use the arrow keys to move to the first unused function register. Press $\boxed{VARS}$ $\boxed{5}$ $\boxed{\blacktriangleright}$ $\boxed{\blacktriangleright}$ $\boxed{7}$ to copy the regression equation found in question 4 into the Y= list. Press $\boxed{+}$ $\boxed{ALPHA}$ [C] to adjust for the vertical shift you made earlier. Press $\boxed{GRAPH}$ to see the data and the two modeling curves. How well does each equation fit the data?

   _____

   _____

6. Describe how the value of B affects the temperature vs. time graph, $y = A\,B^x + C$.

_____

_____

7. Why must the value of B be less than one? What shape does the graph have if B is greater than one?

_____

_____

EXTENSION FOR CALCULUS

Newton's Law of Cooling states that the rate of change of the temperature of a liquid is directly proportional to the difference between its temperature and the temperature of the surroundings. The differential equation is:

$$\frac{dT}{dt} = -k\,(T - T_s)$$

where T_s represents the surrounding temperature. Solve the differential equation (showing your steps) given above to show that $T = (T_0 - T_s)e^{-kt} + T_s$; in this equation, T_0 represents the initial temperature. Explain how the variables in this equation relate to the values of A, B, and C earlier in the experiment. How can both of these be the correct models if the bases are different?

Name _____ Date _____

KEEP IT BOTTLED UP   Activity 11

When two or more chemicals react, other substances such as gases may be produced. The rate at which the reaction takes place can be affected by a number of different factors, including temperature. In this activity, you will see how temperature affects the rate at which an effervescent antacid tablet reacts with water. Here, the gas that is released is carbon dioxide. The rate at which the reaction occurs is a function of the amount of gas which is produced.

You will measure this rate by recording the pressure variations in a closed container as the reaction unfolds using a pressure sensor and a CBL unit. A mathematical equation relating pressure and time will be developed and used to explain how water temperature can affect chemical reaction rates.

YOU NEED:

> 1 CBL Unit
> 1 TI-82 Calculator with Unit-to-Unit Link Cable
> 1 Vernier Pressure Sensor with a long piece of plastic tubing
> 1 Flask (about 500 ml)
> 1 One-Hole Rubber Stopper
> Room-temperature Water and Warm Water (about 200 ml of each)
> Effervescent Antacid Tablets

WARNING: Wear safety goggles at all times! Be careful when removing the stopper from the flask after the data has been collected since pressure will build up while the antacid tablet is being dissolved.

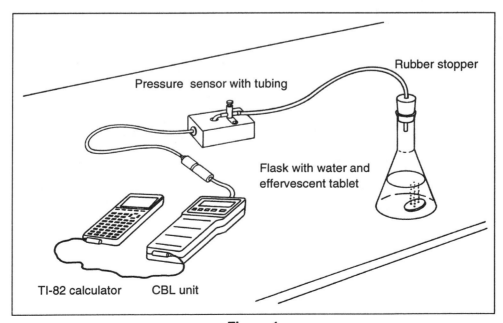

Figure 1

INSTRUCTIONS:

1. Attach the long piece of clear tubing included with the pressure sensor to one of the valves on the sensor. Push the other end of the tubing through a one-hole rubber stopper as shown in Figure 1.

2. You will perform two trials for this experiment, varying the temperature of the water used in each trial. Start with room-temperature water for the first trial, then use warm water for the second trial. Hold the stopper on the flask while the CBL is sampling.

3. Start the BOTTLED program on your TI-82 calculator.

4. Follow the instructions on the TI-82 screen to complete the activity.

ACTIVITY DATA:

The resulting plots should show two sets of linear pressure vs. time data. The room-temperature water data is represented by small data marks and the warm water data is represented by large data marks.

- If you are not satisfied with your results, press CLEAR ENTER to start again.

- If you are satisfied with your results, sketch the data plots in the space in Figure 2.

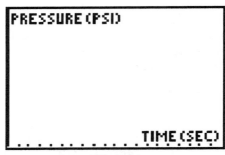

Figure 2

QUESTIONS:

1. Press TRACE to position the cursor on the room-temperature water plot. Use the arrow keys to move along this plot. Identify any two points (x_1, y_1) and (x_2, y_2) and record them below:

	x_1	y_1	x_2	y_2
Room temp water				

Press ▲ to move to the warm water plot and repeat this procedure:

	x_1	y_1	x_2	y_2
Warm water				

Name _____

2. When the coordinates of two points on a line are known, the slope of the line can be computed by finding the difference in y values divided by the difference in x values:

$$slope = \frac{y_2 - y_1}{x_2 - x_1}$$

   Use this formula to compute the slope for each plot. Record your answers below:

   Slope for the room-temperature water plot: _____

   Slope for the warm water plot: _____

3. What is the physical meaning of the slopes of the pressure vs. time plots for this activity?

   _____

4. Press TRACE to position the cursor at the beginning of the room-temperature water plot. Record the y-intercept in the space provided below:

   y-intercept: _____

   What is the physical meaning of this value? Why is this value the same for both plots?

   _____

   _____

5. The slope-intercept form of a linear equation is $y = mx + b$, where m is the slope of the line and b is the y-intercept. Use the information you found above to write linear equations to model the pressure vs. time data:

   Equation for room-temperature water data: _____

   Equation for warm water data: _____

   Press Y= and move the cursor to the first unused function location. Enter the room-temperature water equation here. Move the cursor to the next unused function location and enter the warm water equation. Press GRAPH to see these equations and the data you collected on the same screen. How do the equations fit the data?

   _____

You may wish to adjust your slope and/or intercept values slightly if you are not satisfied with the way the lines fit the data. If you adjust these values, rewrite the modeling equations above.

_____

6. What do you think the pressure vs. time plot would look like after several minutes, if the stopper was left in the flask? Would pressure continue to increase at a steady rate? Explain why or why not.

_____

_____

7. What would the pressure vs. time graph look like if the stopper popped off in the middle of the data collection?

_____

_____

8. For a given water temperature, how do you think the plot would be affected if you used half a tablet? What if you used two tablets?

_____

_____

9. Which plot indicates a faster rate of reaction? How can you tell?

_____

10. How is the rate of reaction related to the water temperature? If you were in need of fast relief using an antacid remedy, which type of water should you use?

_____

_____

CHARGING UP, CHARGING DOWN — Activity 12

A *capacitor* is an electronic component used to store charge. Many of the devices you use on a daily basis, such as radios and televisions, rely on capacitors as part of their electronic circuitry. Cameras use capacitors, too. Charge is transferred from the camera battery to a capacitor and stored there. That charge quickly dissipates to the camera when you press the picture button. The result—a bright flash!

When a capacitor discharges, its voltage drops off very rapidly at first, then begins to level off as the charge dissipates. Mathematically, the action of a discharging capacitor is an exponential phenomenon:

$$y = Ve^{-Kx}$$

where y represents the voltage across the capacitor at any time, x; V is the capacitor's initial voltage; k is a positive constant that depends on the physical characteristics of the capacitor; and e is a special constant called the *base* of the natural logarithm.

The number e is similar to π in that it never repeats and never terminates. It is a popular base used in many exponential expressions.

In this activity, you will collect voltage data from a discharging capacitor using the CBL System and a voltage probe. The capacitor will be connected to another circuit element called a *resistor*, which is used to control the rate at which the capacitor discharges. The voltage data you collect will be analyzed as a way of testing the exponential model described above.

YOU NEED:

        1 CBL Unit
        1 TI-82 Calculator with Unit-to-Unit Link Cable
        1 TI Voltage Probe
        1 220-microfarad Capacitor (Radio Shack catalog #272-1017)
        1 100-kohm Resistor (Radio Shack catalog #271-1347)
        1 9-volt Battery

A diagram for setting up this activity is shown in Figure 1 on the next page.

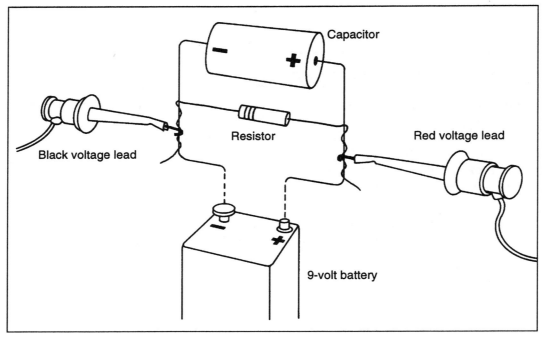

Figure 1

INSTRUCTIONS:

1. Twist the wire ends of the resistor and capacitor together on each side to form a closed loop as shown in Figure 1.

2. Identify the positive and negative sides of the capacitor by carefully examining the markings printed on it. Connect the red CBL voltage lead to the wire coming from the positive side of the capacitor and the black lead to the wire coming from the negative side.

3. Position a 9-volt battery beneath the capacitor-resistor combination so that the positive side of the capacitor is aligned above the positive terminal of the battery, as shown in Figure 1.

4. Start the CHARGE program on your TI-82 calculator.

5. Follow the directions on the TI-82 screen to complete the activity.

ACTIVITY DATA:

Your data plot should show voltages that decrease rapidly at first, then level off.

- If your results are not satisfactory, press [CLEAR] [ENTER] to perform another trial.

- If your results are satisfactory, sketch a plot of your voltage vs. time data on the axes in Figure 2.

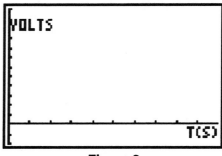

Figure 2

Name _____

QUESTIONS:

1. The theoretical model for the capacitor curve is exponential. We will attempt to fit our data with a curve of the form:

$$y = Ve^{-Kx}$$

where x is time and y is the capacitor voltage. Explain why V represents the y-intercept for this model.

_____

_____

Press TRACE to identify the y-intercept, round it to the nearest hundredth, and record it in the space below:

$$V = \underline{\hspace{3cm}}$$

2. Press Y= and move the cursor to the first unused function register. Enter the expression $V*e^{\wedge}(-KX)$. Access $e^{\wedge}$ by pressing 2nd LN.

After you have entered this equation, press 2nd [QUIT] to return to the home screen. Enter the value of V from question 1, then press STO▶ ALPHA [V] ENTER to store this value to variable V on your calculator.

3. To obtain a good fit, you will need to adjust the value of K. To start, store 1 to the variable K by pressing 1 STO▶ ALPHA [K] ENTER. Press GRAPH to display the data and modeling equation on the same screen.

Repeat this method to store different numbers to the variable K. View the graph for each new value of K that you test. Experiment until you find one that provides a good fit for the data. Record the K value that works best in the space below:

$$K = \underline{\hspace{3cm}}$$

4. Press $\boxed{\text{TRACE}}$ and use the arrow keys to move the cursor along the data plot. Determine the approximate time at which the capacitor voltage reached half its initial value. Record this time value below:

_____ seconds

This value is sometimes called the *half-life* value, denoted $t_{1/2}$. It represents the time required for a quantity that is decaying exponentially to reach half its starting value. There is a simple formula for determining half-life:

$$t_{1/2} = \frac{ln2}{K}$$

Use the formula above and the K value determined in question 3 to compute the value of $t_{1/2}$ and record it below:

$t_{1/2} = $ _____ seconds

How does this value compare to the one you computed?

_____

5. In your own words, describe how the value of V and the value of K affect the voltage vs. time graph, $y = Ve^{-Kx}$.

_____

_____

_____

6. Theoretically, when does the capacitor voltage reach zero in the exponential decay model developed in this activity?

_____

Name _____

EXTENSIONS:

1. Perform a quartic (fourth power) regression on the data you have collected by pressing [STAT] [▶]. Choose **QuartReg** or press [8] to copy the regression command to the home screen. Press [ENTER] to execute this command. Then press [Y=] and use the arrow keys to move the cursor to the first unused function register. Press [VARS] [5] [▶] [▶] [7] to copy the regression equation into the Y= list. Then press [GRAPH] to display the data and the regression curve on the same screen. How well does the quartic curve fit the data?

_____

_____

Even though the quartic expression found above appears to fit the data well locally, it is *not* an appropriate mathematical model. Explain why.
Hint: Press [ZOOM] [3] [ENTER] to examine the end behavior of the quartic function.

_____

_____

2. A more appropiate regression model for this data is an exponential form. To perform an exponential regression on the data you collected, press [STAT] [▶]. Choose **ExpReg** or press [ALPHA] [A] to copy the regression command to the home screen. Press [ENTER] to execute this command. Copy this equation to the Y= list using the procedure described above. Then press [GRAPH] to display the data and the regression curve on the same screen. Does this model provide a good fit?

_____

_____

Notice that the exponential regression equation used by the TI-82 is of the form $y = a\, b^x$ while the modeling equation used in this activity was $y = Ve^{-Kx}$. How are the values of a and V related? How are the values of b and K related?

_____

_____

Name _____ **Date** _____

BOUNCE BACK   Activity 13

When a ball bounces up and down on a flat surface, the maximum height it reaches decreases from bounce to bounce. In fact, it decreases in a very predictable way for most types of balls. The mathematical relationship between the maximum height attained by the ball on a given bounce (which we will call the *rebound height*) and number of bounces that have occurred since the ball was released is exponential:

$$y = hp^x$$

where y represents the rebound height, x represents the bounce number, h is the release height, and p is a constant that depends on the physical characteristics of the ball used.

In this exercise, you will collect motion data for a bouncing ball using the CBL System and a sonic motion detector. You will then analyze this data in an attempt to verify the mathematical relationship stated above.

YOU NEED:

      1 CBL Unit
      1 TI-82 Calculator with Unit-to-Unit Link Cable
      1 Vernier CBL Motion Detector
      A Ball (racquetballs and basketballs work well)

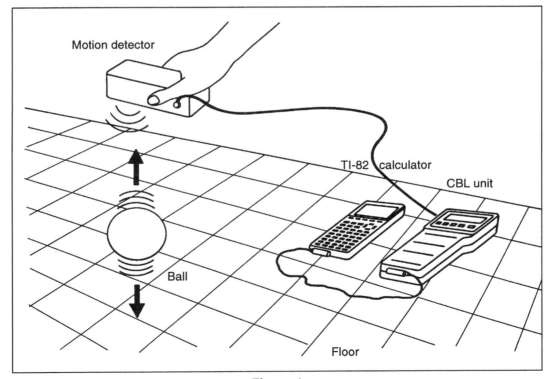

Figure 1

INSTRUCTIONS:

When instructed to hold the ball under the motion detector, be sure to hold the detector 5 to 6 feet above the floor, parallel to it, as shown in Figure 1. *Bounce the ball on a smooth, level surface.* Do not allow anything to obstruct the path between the motion detector and the ball while data is being collected.

1. Start the BALL program on your TI-82 calculator.

2. Follow the instructions on the TI-82 screen to complete the activity.

ACTIVITY DATA:

1. If you have fewer than five consecutive bounces, you will need to perform another trial. In this case, start with a smaller initial height.

   - If you are dissatisfied with your results, press CLEAR ENTER, return to the home screen, and rerun the program.

   - If you are satisfied with your results, sketch a plot of your distance vs. time data on the axes in Figure 2. Be sure to include the axes on your sketch.

Figure 2

2. In this activity, we wish to examine how the rebound height of the ball varies from bounce to bounce. Press TRACE. Use the arrow keys to move the cursor along the bouncing ball data. Start with the initial release height and record consecutive rebound heights (y values at the crest of each parabolic section) for each numbered bounce in the table below. Round your answers to the nearest hundredth.

   Note: You only need to record rebound data for the first five bounces.

Bounce Number (x values)	Rebound Height (y values)
0 (starting height)	
1	
2	
3	
4	
5	

3. Now you need to enter the data in the table above into lists L_3 and L_4 of your TI-82 calculator. Press STAT ENTER ▶ ▶ to access the L_3 list editor. If L_3 is not empty, press ▲ to move the cursor to the top of the list, and then press CLEAR ENTER to clear the list. Now enter the bounce number values from above into list L_3. Press ▶ to move to list L_4. Clear L_4 and enter the corresponding rebound heights.

---

4. Press [2nd] [STAT PLOT] [ENTER] to access the screen shown in Figure 3. Adjust the settings to match those shown in the display. Use the arrow keys to move around the screen, and press [ENTER] to select the settings. Press [ZOOM] [9] to see a plot of rebound height vs. bounce number. Sketch the resulting plot in Figure 4 below. You will need to draw in the axes and scale markers on your sketch.

Figure 3

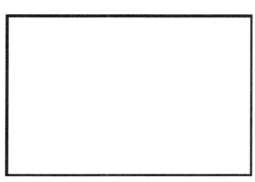

Figure 4

QUESTIONS:

1. The theoretical model for the bouncing ball data recorded in the table above is exponential. We will attempt to fit this data with a curve of the form:

$$y = H\,P^x$$

where x represents the bounce number and y represents the corresponding rebound height. In this model, H represents the starting height. Press [GRAPH] [TRACE]. The first value on the curve is the y-intercept (the initial height). Record this value in the space provided below:

$$H = \underline{\hspace{3cm}}$$

Use the equation $y = H\,P^x$ to explain why H is the value of the y-intercept.

_____

2. Press $\boxed{Y=}$ and move the cursor to the first available function register. Enter the equation $Y = H*P^\wedge X$ and then press $\boxed{\text{2nd}}$ [QUIT] to return to the home screen. Enter the value of H found above, then press $\boxed{\text{STO}\blacktriangleright}$ $\boxed{\text{ALPHA}}$ [H] $\boxed{\text{ENTER}}$ to store this value to variable H on your calculator. You will try to determine a value for P through trial and error. Start with an initial value of $P = 1$ by pressing $\boxed{1}$ $\boxed{\text{STO}\blacktriangleright}$ $\boxed{\text{ALPHA}}$ [P] $\boxed{\text{ENTER}}$. Then press $\boxed{\text{GRAPH}}$ to display the data and curve on the same screen.

To obtain a good fit, you will need to adjust the value of P. Use the method described above to store different numbers to the variable P. View the graph for each new value of P that you test. Experiment until you find one that provides a good fit for the data. Record the P value that works best in the space below:

$$P = \underline{\hspace{2in}}$$

3. We just considered the equation:

$$y = H\,P^x$$

where y is the rebound height and x is the bounce number, as before. Dividing by H and taking the natural logarithm of both sides gives:

$$\frac{y}{H} = P^x$$

$$ln\,\frac{y}{H} = ln\,P^x$$

Simplifying using logarithm rules and basic algebra:

$$ln\,\frac{y}{H} = x\,ln\,P$$

$$ln\,y - ln\,H = x\,ln\,P$$

$$\boxed{ln\,y = (ln\,P)x + ln\,H}$$

That is, a graph of $ln\,y$ vs. x is linear with a slope of $ln\,P$ and a y-intercept of $ln\,H$. We can use the data we have collected during this activity to make this graph.

To take the natural logarithm of the rebound heights (y values), press $\boxed{\text{LN}}$ [L$_4$] $\boxed{\text{STO}\blacktriangleright}$ [L$_5$] $\boxed{\text{ENTER}}$. The $ln\,y$ values are now stored in list L$_5$.

Name _____

4. Press [2nd] [STAT PLOT] to access the screen shown in Figure 5. Adjust the settings to match those shown in the display. Use the arrow keys to move around the screen, and press [ENTER] to select the settings.

   Press [Y=] to access the function editor screen. Notice that the equation you graphed in question 3 is selected; that is, the equals sign is highlighted for this equation. Use the arrow keys to move on top of the highlighted equals sign and press [ENTER] to

Figure 5

un-select this equation. Press [ZOOM] [9] to see a plot of *ln y* vs. *x*. Sketch the resulting plot in the space in Figure 6 below. You will need to draw in the axes and scale markers on your sketch.

Figure 6

5. The TI-82 calculator has a built-in feature that allows it to compute the best-fitting line through a set of data. To perform this operation, press [STAT] [▷]. Select **LinReg** or press [5] [2nd] [L$_3$] [,] [2nd] [L$_5$] [ENTER]. Copy the values which appear on your calculator screen into the matching table in Figure 7.

   Press [Y=] and use the arrow keys to move the cursor to the first available function register. Press [VARS] [5] [▷] [▷] [7] to copy the regression line equation into the Y= list. Press [GRAPH] to display the data and regression line on the same screen. How well does the equation fit the data?

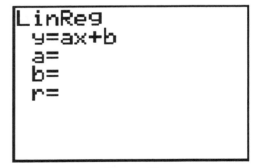

Figure 7

_____

_____

6. Use the values of P and H found in questions 1 and 2 to compute $ln\ P$ and $ln\ H$. Record these values in the table below:

ln P	
ln H	

How do these values compare with the linear regression constants a and b from the previous question? Do they match? Explain why they should match.
Hint: Compare the equations $ln\ y = (ln\ P)\ x + ln\ H$ and $y = a * x + b$.

_____

_____

7. Suppose that you repeat this activity using a ball that is not as resilient as the ball you used. For example, if you used a basketball, imagine that some air is let out of it, then the exercise is repeated. How would the constants H and P in the equation $y = H\ P^x$ be affected by this, if at all?

_____

_____

8. Use any one of the models developed in this activity to determine the smallest number of bounces required for the rebound height to be less than 10% of its starting height. Remember that the number of bounces must be an integer value. Record your answer below:

Number of bounces: _____

SOUR CHEMISTRY   Activity 14

Chemists quantify the relative acidity or alkalinity of a solution by measuring its pH on a scale ranging from 0 to 14. A neutral substance, such as distilled water, has a pH of exactly 7. A pH lower than 7 suggests an acidic solution, while a pH higher than 7 indicates that a solution is basic.

Different pH levels must be maintained throughout the body in order for a person to remain healthy. Excessively high or low pH levels often result in discomfort or irritation. For example, common indigestion or upset stomach usually indicates the presence of excessive amounts of stomach acids. This condition can sometimes be alleviated by ingesting an antacid tablet, or by drinking a solution such as Alka-Seltzer® and water, designed to neutralize these acids and raise the pH level in the stomach.

In this activity, the conditions found in an acid stomach will be simulated using a solution of lemon juice and water. The effectiveness of an antacid remedy will be tested by monitoring the pH of the solution after an effervescent antacid tablet has been added to it. The resulting data will be modeled using a modified exponential function.

YOU NEED:

> 1 CBL Unit
> 1 TI-82 Calculator with Unit-to-Unit Link Cable
> 1 Vernier pH Meter System with CBL-DIN adapter
> 7 oz. Drinking Cup
> Distilled Water (about 3 or 4 ounces per trial)
> Lemon Juice (about 10 drops per trial)
> Eyedropper
> Effervescent Antacid Tablets (for example, Alka-Seltzer®) one per trial

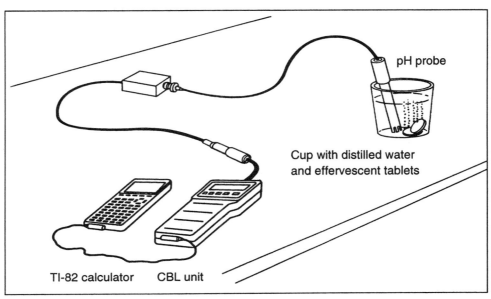

Figure 1

INSTRUCTIONS:

You will be instructed how to mix the lemon-juice-water solution when you run the activity program. If you decide to perform more than one trial, thoroughly rinse out the cup you are using before repeating the activity. Any residue in the cup may cause erroneous pH readings.

1. Start the CHEM program on your TI-82 calculator.

2. Follow the instructions on the TI-82 screen to complete the activity.

ACTIVITY DATA:

Your data plot should show pH values that increase rapidly at first, then level off.

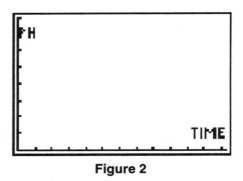
Figure 2

- If your data plot is not satisfactory, press CLEAR ENTER to do another trial. If you need to perform another trial, be sure to thoroughly rinse out the cup you are using before repeating the activity since residue in the cup may cause erroneous pH readings.

- If you are satisfied with the data you've collected, sketch a plot of your pH vs. time data on the axes provided in Figure 2.

QUESTIONS:

1. The theoretical model for the pH vs. time data is a modified exponential function. We will attempt to fit our data with a curve of the form:

$$y = A(1 - B^x) + C$$

where y represents the solution's pH at any time, x. In this model, C represents the solution's initial pH, that is, the y-intercept. Press TRACE and identify this initial value. Round the value to the nearest tenth and record it in the space below:

$$C = \underline{\hspace{2cm}}$$

2. Notice that, as time increases, the pH readings begin the approach a constant value as the curve flattens. Press GRAPH, then press 2nd [DRAW] 3 to put a horizontal marker on the screen. Use the ▲ ▼ keys to move this marker up and down on the screen. Use it to estimate the y value that the pH vs. time curve is approaching as the time values become larger and larger. Record this value in the space below:

pH approach value = \underline{\hspace{2cm}}

Name _____

3. The approach value you just found is related to the sum of the constants in the modeling equation. Given the fact that $0 < B < 1$, explain why the pH approach value is equal to $A + C$.

_____

_____

Use the information above, together with the approach value found in question 2 and the constant C found in question 1, to solve for A. Record this value in the space provided:

$$A = \text{_____}$$

4. Press [Y=] and move the cursor to the first unused function register. Enter the expression $A*(1 - B\char`\^X) + C$ and then press [2nd] [QUIT] to return to the home screen. Enter the value of A found above, then press [STO▶] [ALPHA] [A] [ENTER] to store this value to variable A on your calculator. Repeat this procedure to store variable C.

To obtain a good fit, you will need to adjust the value of B. Use the method described above to store different numbers to the variable B. Start with $B = 0.5$. View the graph for each value of B you test by pressing [GRAPH] after a new value has been stored to B. Experiment until you find one that provides a good fit for the data. Record the B value that works best in the space below. Round this value to the nearest hundredth.

$$B = \text{_____}$$

5. Use your own words to briefly describe how the value of B affects the shape of the modeling curve.

_____

_____

6. How would adding more drops of lemon juice to the starting solution affect the resulting plot of pH vs. time for this activity? Which variable(s) in the equation $y = A(1 - B^x) + C$ would change, if any?
   Hint: Adding more lemon juice would make the initial solution more acidic (that is, it would have a lower pH at the start).

_____

_____

7. How would adding two antacid tablets to the lemon-water solution rather than one tablet affect the shape of the pH vs. time curve? Would any of the constants in the equation $y = A(1 - B^x) + C$ be different? Explain your reasoning.

_____

_____

8. Suppose you are asked to compare the effectiveness of two different brands of antacid tablets. What variable in the modeling equation $y = A(1 - B^x) + C$ would give the best indication of how well a tablet works?
   Hint: Which variable would affect the speed of the relief?

_____

_____

_____

EXTENSION:

The equation used in this activity, $y = -Ab^x + (A + C)$, is actually a modified version of the basic exponential equation, $y = AB^x$. Describe how $y = AB^x$ can be transformed into the desired modeling equation using reflections and shifts.
Hint: Work backwards by distributing A and re-grouping to obtain $y = -Ab^x + (A + C)$.

Name _____ **Date** _____

LIGHTS OUT!   Activity 15

A rocking chair moving back and forth, a ringing telephone, and water dripping from a leaky faucet are all examples of *periodic* phenomena. They are called periodic because they can be characterized by rhythmic cycles occurring in regular time intervals. The time required to observe one complete cycle of the behavior is called the *period*. The number of times the cycle occurs per unit time is known as the *frequency*.

In the following activities, you will use the CBL and a light sensor to collect data for two different types of period phenomena. You will then analyze this data with your calculator to find the period and the frequency of the observed behavior.

YOU NEED:

> 1 CBL Unit
> 1 TI-82 Calculator with Unit-to-Unit Link Cable
> 1 TI Light Probe
> 1 Single-Bulb Fluorescent Light Source
> 1 Stopwatch or wristwatch with capability of timing to the tenth of a second

ACTIVITY PART 1:

In this activity, you will point a light sensor towards a light source such as a window or an overhead lamp. To start, the end of the sensor will be covered by your thumb. When the CBL is activated, you will begin alternately lifting your thumb from the sensor and re-covering it. Light intensity readings will be collected by the CBL and displayed on the screen of your calculator as you gather the data.

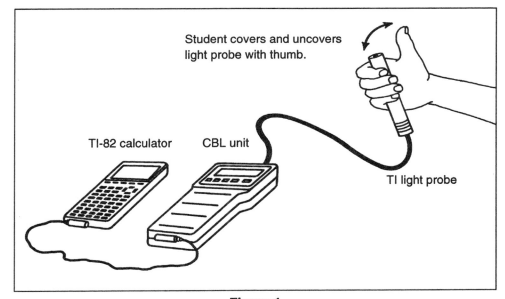

Figure 1

INSTRUCTIONS:

1. Hold the light sensor inside your fist with its end protruding about 1/2 inch, as shown in Figure 1. The end of the sensor must be pointed towards a light source while the CBL is sampling.

2. After the CBL has been activated, you will cover and uncover the probe in regular time intervals. For the first trial, repeat the cover-uncover pattern about once a second. You might consider counting out loud, "one thousand one, one thousand two, ..." to keep the time intervals uniform.

3. Start the LIGHT1 program on your calculator.

4. Follow the instructions on the TI-82 screen to complete the activity.

PART 1 DATA:

Your data should show intensity levels which start at a large value then alternate between this value and zero in a regular pattern. The time interval between cycles should appear to be relatively constant.

- If your data is not satisfactory, press CLEAR ENTER to perform another trial.

- If your data is satisfactory, sketch a plot of your data on the axes in Figure 2.

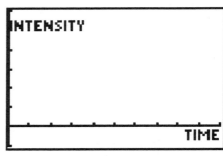

Figure 2

QUESTIONS:

1. For the data plot above, what do the plateaus represent? What do the minimum values represent?

_____

_____

2. On your calculator press TRACE and use the arrow keys to move along the plot. The x-values shown at the bottom of your calculator screen are times and the y-values are intensities. Trace to the first time value corresponding to zero intensity (or very near zero) following the initial plateau. Store this value in your calculator as A by pressing X,T,Θ STO▶ ALPHA [A] ENTER. Record this time value below, rounding to the nearest hundredth of a second:

$$A = \text{_____ seconds}$$

3. Press TRACE to return to your data. Use the arrow keys to move to the first time value corresponding to zero intensity (or very near zero) following the last complete plateau shown on the screen. Store this value in your calculator as B by pressing X,T,Θ STO▶ ALPHA [B] ENTER. Record this time value below, rounding to the nearest hundredth of a second:

$$B = \text{_____ seconds}$$

4. Press GRAPH. How many cycles were completed between time *A* and time *B*? That is, how many times did you uncover then re-cover the sensor during this time interval? Record this number below:

Cycles completed: _____

5. The *period* is the time required to complete one cycle. Find the average period by dividing the difference between *A* and *B*, *(B - A)*, by the number of cycles completed during this interval. Record this value below, rounding to the nearest hundredth of a second:

Period: _____ seconds

6. While the period represents the number of seconds per cycle, the *frequency* is the number of cycles per second. Find the frequency of the cover-uncover motion by taking the reciprocal of the period value you just found. Press x^{-1} ENTER to do this. Record this value below.

Frequency: _____ cycles per second

7. Multiply your frequency by 60 and discuss what this number represents.

_____

_____

EXTENSION 1:

Run the LIGHT1 program again. This time, increase the period of time during which you uncover and re-cover the sensor. Before you collect and analyze the data, predict how this modification will affect the period. How will it affect the frequency?

ACTIVITY PART 2:

For this experiment you will point the light sensor at a single fluorescent light bulb and record its intensity for a very short period of time. The resulting plot of intensity vs. time is interesting because it shows that fluorescent lights do not stay on continuously but rather flicker off and on very rapidly in a periodic way. Since the human eye cannot distinguish between flashes that occur more than about 50 times a second, the light appears to be on all the time. The data you collect will be used to determine the period and frequency at which the bulb flickers.

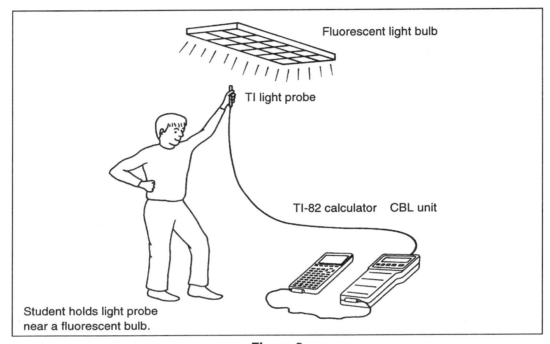

Figure 3

INSTRUCTIONS:

1. Locate a single fluorescent bulb to use as a light source.

2. Start the program LIGHT2 on your calculator.

3. Follow the instructions on the TI-82 screen to complete the data gathering portion of this experiment.

PART 2 DATA:

Your data should resemble a series of uniformly spaced parabolas of approximately the same size.

- If your results are not satisfactory, press [CLEAR] [ENTER] to begin another trial.

- If your results are satisfactory, sketch a plot of your data on the axes in Figure 4.

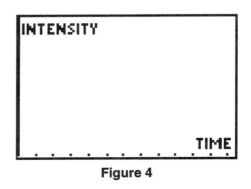

Figure 4

Name _____

QUESTIONS:

1. From the intensity vs. time graph on your calculator, it appears that light intensity values are rising and falling in a regular pattern. What do the peaks or maximum values on your data set represent in terms of the flashing bulb? What do the minimum values represent?

_____

_____

2. To calculate the period of the bulb's flicker, you need to find the time interval corresponding to one complete on-off cycle. One way to do this is to determine the time between any two consecutive minimum values.

   Press [TRACE] to return to your data. Use the arrow keys to move the cursor to an apparent minimum value near the center of the plot. The x-value at the bottom of the screen represents the time when this minimum occurred. Store this value in your calculator as A by pressing [STO▸] [ALPHA] [A] [ENTER].

   Press [TRACE] again and move the cursor to the apparent minimum immediately to the right of the one you just examined. Press [X,T,θ] to copy this time value to the home screen. Press [–] [ALPHA] [A] [ENTER] to subtract A from this time value. The difference represents the time between consecutive minimums; that is, the period. Record this value below:

   Period: _____ seconds

3. The period value found in question 2 represents the time required for one complete on-off cycle; that is, the seconds per cycle. Find the frequency (cycles per second) by taking the reciprocal of the period. Press [x^{-1}] [ENTER] to do this. Record the frequency below:

   Frequency: _____ cycles per second

4. In the United States, electric utilities use a current whose frequency is 60 cycles per second. Is this consistent with your findings from this activity?
   Hint: The so-called alternating current used in households actually switches polarity two times per cycle.

_____

_____

5. If the light source really is turning off every half-cycle, why isn't the minimum y-value on your intensity vs. time plot equal to zero?

_____

_____

EXTENSION 2:

The fluorescent light bulb intensity vs. time data you collected in this activity can be modeled with an absolute value sinusoidal equation of the form:

$$y = A \mid sin\ (B(x - C)) \mid + D$$

Can you determine appropriate values for A, B, C, and D so that this equation properly models your data? How do the frequencies of $y = A\ sin\ (B(x - C)) + D$ and $y = A \mid sin\ (B(x - C)) \mid + D$ compare? How do the periods compare?

Name _____   **Date** _____

TIC, TOC   Activity 16

Pendulum motion has fascinated people for hundreds of years. Galileo studied pendulum motion by watching a swinging chandelier and timing it with his pulse. Jean Foucault proved that the earth rotates by using a long pendulum which swung in the same plane and showed that the earth rotated underneath it. The Foucault Pendulum is now an attraction in many science museums around the country.

Pendulum motion for small angles is shown to approximate simple harmonic motion and produce a sinusoidal pattern. In this experiment, you will use a motion detector to plot the position vs. time graph for a simple pendulum. You will time the motion to calculate the period, and use a ruler to measure the maximum displacement. You will then use your data to find an equation that describes the position vs. time graph.

YOU NEED:

        1 CBL Unit
        1 TI-82 Calculator with Unit-to-Unit Link Cable
        1 Vernier CBL Motion Detector
        1 Stopwatch
        1 Pendulum Bob
        1 Meter Stick
        String

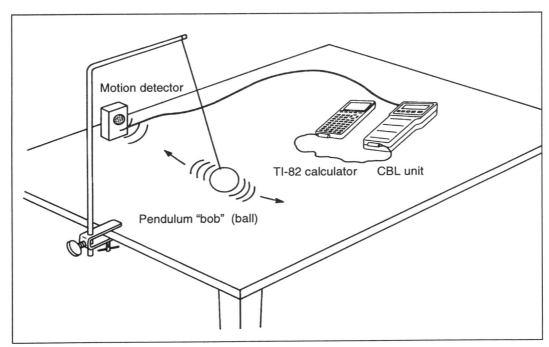

Figure 1

INSTRUCTIONS:

1. Hang a pendulum as instructed by your teacher (see Figure 1). Make sure that the bottom of the pendulum is several centimeters from the top of the table or desk. It is best to elevate the detector and keep the pendulum high enough so that the motion detector does not detect the table or desk. Position a meter stick along the table so that the zero point is at the motion detector.

2. Before the data collection begins, there are two measurements that need to be made and recorded:

   - Measure the distance between the pendulum and the motion detector in centimeters. Be sure that the distance is at least 75 cm. Record your measurement in question 1 of the Activity Data section below.

   - Determine how far you will pull the pendulum away from its original position. This distance should not be more than 20 cm. Record the distance in question 2 of the Activity Data section.

3. One cycle of the pendulum consists of the motion for one complete swing back and forth. During this activity, you will use a stopwatch to time the pendulum for ten complete cycles. The easiest way to do this is to begin the stopwatch when the pendulum bob is farthest from the detector and count one cycle when it returns to that spot. Record the time for ten cycles in question 3 of the Activity Data section.

4. Run the program TICTOC on your TI-82 calculator.

5. Follow the directions on the TI-82 screen to complete the activity.

ACTIVITY DATA:

1. What is the distance from the motion detector to the pendulum?

   _____cm.

2. What distance was the pendulum pulled back from its stationary position?

   _____cm.

3. What was the time for ten complete cycles of the pendulum?

   _____ seconds.

4. The resulting distance vs. time plot should be sinusoidal.

   - If you are dissatisfied with your results, press CLEAR ENTER to collect new data.
   - If you are satisfied with your results, sketch a plot of your distance vs. time graph in the space in Figure 2.

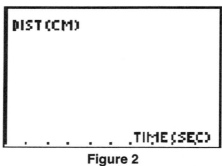

Figure 2

Name _____

QUESTIONS:

In this activity, you will first fit the curve with a sinusoidal curve of the form:

$$Y = A \cos B(X - C) + D.$$

1. The constant, *A*, represents the *amplitude,* which is the distance from a high or low point on the curve to the horizontal center axis of the curve. Your measurement taken of the distance the pendulum was pulled away from its at-rest position (as recorded in number 2 above) is the amplitude. Store this value to the variable *A* on your calculator by entering the number followed by [STO▸] [ALPHA] [A] [ENTER]. Record your value below.

$$A = \underline{\hspace{2cm}} \text{ cm}$$

2. The *period* of the pendulum is the time for one complete cycle. Use the time for ten complete cycles that was recorded in number 3 above to determine the period.

$$\text{Period} = \underline{\hspace{2cm}} \text{ seconds}$$

Explain your method and discuss why ten cycles were used rather than just one.

_____

_____

3. The constant, *B*, represents the number of cycles the sinusoid makes during the natural period of the cosine function. Find *B* by taking 2π (the natural period of the cosine function) divided by the period (the time for one cycle). Store this value as B on your calculator by entering the value followed by [STO▸] [ALPHA] [B] [ENTER]. Record your value for *B* in the space below.

$$B = \underline{\hspace{2cm}}$$

4. The constant, *C*, represents the horizontal shift of the sinusoid. Since the cosine curve naturally begins with a maximum value, a value for *C* is easy to find. Press [TRACE] and use the arrow keys to move the cursor to any maximum value. The *C* value is the horizontal distance that the curve is shifted over which corresponds to the *x*-value at this point. Press [X] [STO▸] [ALPHA] [C] [ENTER] to store this value of *X* as *C*. Record the value below.

$$C = \underline{\hspace{2cm}}$$

5. The constant, D, represents the vertical shift of the data from the x-axis. The center line or axis of your data represents the stationary position of the pendulum. The distance from the motion detector to the pendulum (as recorded in number 1 of the Activity Data section) is the value of the constant D. Store this value in your calculator by entering the value followed by [STO▸] [ALPHA] [D] [ENTER]. Record the value below.

$$D = \underline{\hspace{2cm}} \text{ cm}$$

6. Press [Y=] and enter $A \cos B(X - C) + D$ in the first available function register. Press [GRAPH]. How well does the equation fit your data? If your fit is acceptable, write the equation below and give the reasons for any slight discrepancies. If the equation does not produce a reasonable fit, analyze which of your variable values produces the error and recalculate it. Discuss the changes that you make and why you were forced to make them. Finally, write out the equation that produced a good fit.

_____

_____

7. How would the values of A, B, C, and D change if you use a sine curve to fit the data? Predict the values below, explaining your reasoning for each.

_____

_____

_____

_____

8. Write the equation which models this motion in the form $y = A \sin B(X - C) + D$.

_____

Test your prediction by storing any new values for A, B, C, or D in your calculator. Press [Y=] and edit your cosine equation. Move the cursor so that it is over the *cos* and press [SIN]. Then press [GRAPH]. How well does this equation fit your data? Give a reason for any discrepancies. Re-evaluate the values for the variables, if necessary.

_____

_____

Name _____

9. Explain the physical interpretations of the variables *A*, *B*, *C*, and *D* as they relate to the swinging pendulum and the equation $Y = A \cos B(X - C) + D$.

_____

_____

EXTENSION FOR CALCULUS:

Once you have an equation for the position vs. time graph of the pendulum motion, take the derivative of the equation. This represents the velocity of the pendulum at any time *t*. How does the velocity vs. time graph compare with the position vs. time graph? When during the pendulum motion is the velocity zero? When is the velocity a maximum?

The derivative of velocity is *acceleration*. Take the second derivative of the position equation. Describe the position and velocity when the acceleration is a maximum. Do the same when the acceleration is zero.

Give a general description of the pendulum's position, velocity, and acceleration when the bob is passing through the at-rest position and when it is farthest from the detector.

Name _____ Date _____

SWINGING ELLIPSES   Activity 17

Any ellipse centered at the origin can be expressed in the form:

$$\frac{x^2}{a^2} + \frac{y^2}{b^2} = 1$$

where $\pm a$ and $\pm b$ represent the ellipse's x- and y-intercepts respectively. Knowing the intercepts of an ellipse in standard position, then, it is possible to find its equation.

To graph an ellipse on the TI-82 calculator, the expression above must first be solved for y to obtain:

$$y = \pm b \sqrt{1 - \frac{x^2}{a^2}}$$

This equation is entered into the calculator in two parts, one expression for the positive part (upper half of the ellipse) and one for the negative part (lower half of the ellipse), as shown in Figure 1.

In this activity, you will use the CBL system and a motion detector to record the motion of a swinging pendulum. The elliptical nature of the resulting plot of velocity vs. position will be investigated and modeled mathematically.

Figure 1

YOU NEED:

       1 CBL Unit
       1 TI-82 Calculator with Unit-to-Unit Link Cable
       1 Vernier CBL Motion Detector
       1 Pendulum Bob
       String (about 4 feet)

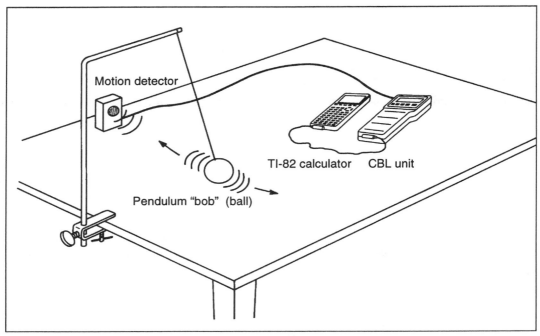

Figure 2

INSTRUCTIONS:

1. Connect the pendulum bob to the string and suspend it from a support as shown in Figure 2. Arrange the motion detector so that the bob swings back and forth in front of it and comes no closer than two feet to the detector.

2. Start the SWING program on your TI-82 calculator.

3. Follow the instructions on the TI-82 screen to complete the activity.

ACTIVITY DATA:

The resulting plot of velocity vs. position should be elliptical.

- If you are dissatisfied with your results, press CLEAR ENTER to start again.

- If you are satisfied with your results, make a rough sketch of the velocity vs. position data you collected in the space in Figure 3.

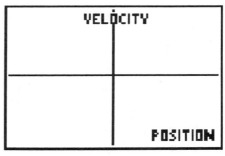

Figure 3

Name _____

QUESTIONS:

1. Press TRACE. Move the cursor along your velocity vs. position plot and identify, to the nearest hundredth of a foot, the x- and y-intercepts. Record these values in the table below.

First x-intercept	Second x-intercept	First y-intercept	Second y-intercept

2. Average the absolute values of the x-intercepts and record this value in the space below as a:

$$a = \text{\underline{\hspace{2cm}}}$$

Average the absolute values of the y-intercepts and record this value in the space below as b:

$$b = \text{\underline{\hspace{2cm}}}$$

3. Press Y= and move the cursor to the first available function register. Enter the ellipse equations exactly as shown in Figure 1. Press 2nd [QUIT] to return to the home screen. Enter the value of a from above and store it to the variable A on your calculator by pressing STO▶ ALPHA [A] ENTER. Repeat this procedure to store the value of b to the variable B.

4. Press GRAPH to see the data and curves on the same screen. Update your original sketch in the Activity Data section to include the curves depicted on the calculator screen. Use a different color pencil or pen to distinguish these curves from your original data set. How well do the curves fit the data?

_____

5. At what point in the pendulum's swing is its velocity the largest? Where is the velocity zero? How are these values related to the x- and y-intercepts?

_____

_____

_____

6. How would the data change if the *amplitude* (the largest distance from the middle position) of the pendulum's swing were increased? How would this change affect the values of the constants a and b, if at all?

_____

_____

_____

EXTENSION:

Show how the algebraic expression $y = \pm b \sqrt{1 - \dfrac{x^2}{a^2}}$ used in this activity can be derived from the ellipse equation $\dfrac{x^2}{a^2} + \dfrac{y^2}{b^2} = 1$.

Name _____ Date _____

STEPPING TO THE GREATEST INTEGER   Activity 18

Not all mathematical functions have smooth, continuous graphs. In fact, some of the most interesting functions contain jumps and gaps. One such function is called the *greatest integer function*, denoted

$y = int\ x$ or $y = [x]$. It is defined as follows:

int x *equals the largest integer less than or equal to x.*

The graph of $y = int\ x$ yields a series of steps and jumps as shown in Figure 1. This graph was made on the TI-82 calculator and then modified to show which points on the graph are included (closed circles) and which are not (open circles).

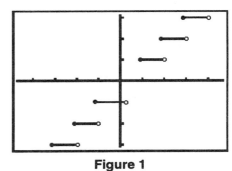

Figure 1

In this activity, you will create a function similar to the greatest integer function graph by having a group of students stand in a line in front of a motion detector connected to a CBL and then step aside one by one. The equation for this graph, in the general form:

$$y = A\ int\ (Bx) + C$$

will be determined by finding appropriate values for the constants A, B, and C.

YOU NEED:

      1 CBL Unit
      1 TI-82 Calculator with Unit-to-Unit Link Cable
      1 Vernier CBL Motion Detector

See set-up instructions on the next page.

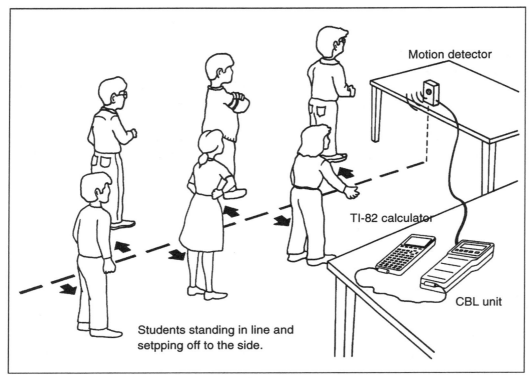

Figure 2

INSTRUCTIONS:

1. In this activity, a group of students will step from in front of a motion detector to create a step graph. To start, line up six students in front of the detector as shown in Figure 2. Be sure that the spacing between students is uniform (about a foot) and that the first student in line is no closer than two feet from the detector.

2. Once the detector is activated, students should step aside in evenly spaced time intervals so that the lengths of the segments appearing on the distance vs. time plot are uniform. To help gauge the pace, you might have one student tell the others when to step aside by counting out loud every two or three seconds. **Be patient; it may take several trials to obtain a plot that resembles a greatest integer function.**

3. Start the STEPPING program on your TI-82 calculator.

4. Follow the instructions on the TI-82 screen to complete the activity.

ACTIVITY DATA:

Your plot should show a series of steps which roughly resemble Figure 1.

- If you are dissatisfied with your results, press CLEAR ENTER to start again.

- If you are satisfied with your results, make a rough sketch of the distance vs. time data you collected on the axes provided in Figure 3.

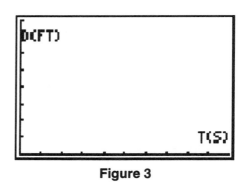

Figure 3

Name _____

1. You will fit the data using the equation $y = A\ int\ (Bx) + C$. Compare the graph of the data with the graph of the greatest integer function in Figure 1. Observe that the initial step of your function is raised compared with the step of the greatest integer function between [0,1]. Your data is shifted vertically compared with this function. Press [TRACE] to trace along your first step. The Y value along the step is the value of the vertical shift which corresponds to C in the equation. To store this Y value as C on the home screen, perform the following key strokes. From the graph, press [ALPHA] [Y] [STO▶] [ALPHA] [C] [ENTER]. Record the value of C below.

$$C = \underline{\hspace{2cm}}$$

2. Press the [GRAPH] key to return to the graph. The value of A in the equation causes a vertical stretch or shrink which corresponds to the vertical distance between the steps. Press [TRACE] and use the arrow keys to move the cursor along the first step until the cursor jumps to the second step. To find the vertical distance between the steps, subtract C, the height of the first step, from the height of the second step by performing the following key strokes. From the graph, with the cursor on the second step, press [ALPHA] [Y] [−] [ALPHA] [C] [STO▶] [ALPHA] [A] [ENTER]. Record the value of A below.

$$A = \underline{\hspace{2cm}}$$

3. Now try guessing different values of B. The value of B affects the horizontal stretch or shrink. Begin by letting $B = 1$. Store this value by pressing [1] [STO▶] [ALPHA] [B] [ENTER] on the home screen.

4. Check to see how well your values of A, B, and C fit your data. Press [Y=] and move the cursor to the first unused function register. Enter the equation:

$$Y = A\ int\ (Bx) + C$$

The *int* operation is obtained by pressing [MATH] [▶] [4]. Then press [GRAPH] to see the data and the graph of your equation together. It is likely that this graph does not fit the data well. You will probably need to adjust the value of B and, possibly, make slight adjustments to the values of A and C.

5. Modify the constants A, B, and C by storing different values to them as described above. Use the information in the box at the right to decide how each constant should be changed. Remember, this is a trial-and-error process, so it may be frustrating at times.

> A causes a vertical stretch or shrink
>
> B causes a horizontal stretch or shrink
>
> C causes the graph to be shifted up or down vertically

Change the constants one at a time. View the new graph after each adjustment. When you are satisfied with the fit you have obtained, record the correct values for A, B, and C in the table below:

A	
B	
C	

QUESTIONS:

1. What is the physical significance of the value of C in the equation $Y = A \, int \, (Bx) + C$?

_____

2. What is the physical significance of the value of A in the equation?

_____

3. How is the value of B related to the length of time between the steps?
   Hint: Examine the value of $1/B$.

_____

4. Suppose a new group of students repeats this activity under the following conditions. The students are farther away at the start, they are spaced closer together, and they step off more quickly. State whether each constant A, B, and C would increase or decrease.

_____

_____

_____

5. The greatest integer function has some interesting business applications. Suppose a phone company charges $0.25 for the first minute and $0.15 for each additional minute for a call to a certain exchange. Develop a formula, involving the greatest integer function, to describe the amount charged as a function of the amount of time spent on the phone. Remember, if a customer talks for 3.01 or 3.99 minutes, they are charged for 4 minutes of conversation. Give the appropriate formula below.

_____

6. Is the formula developed in question 5 correct if a person talks for an integer number of minutes? If not, what is wrong with the formula in this case? If necessary, modify it to make it correct in all cases. Explain your method.

_____

_____

_____

_____

EXTENSIONS:

Consider the equation $y = 3\ int\ (0.25x) + 5$. Discuss the significance of the constants in this equation. Write a set of instructions describing the way a group of students would have to move in front of a motion detector to create a data set for which this equation would be an appropriate model. Run the STEPPING program and follow the set of instructions that you developed. Enter the given equation in the Y= list. How well does this equation fit the data you collected?

Name other real world situations that can be modeled using the greatest integer function.

Name _____ **Date** _____

MATCH IT, GRAPH IT   Activity 19

Graphs of real-world data cannot always be described with only one simple equation. Often times, the graph is made up of separate pieces which together describe a problem or event. If you move back and forth in front of a motion detector, your motion would be described in separate pieces which together would describe the total motion. Equations which are defined in pieces are called *piecewise-defined functions*.

In this activity, you will match your motion to a given graph by moving back and forth in front of a motion detector. You will then describe your motion by writing a piecewise-defined equation for the motion.

YOU NEED:

       1 CBL Unit
       1 TI-82 Calculator with Unit-to-Unit Link Cable
       1 Vernier CBL Motion Detector
       1 Meter Stick
       Masking Tape

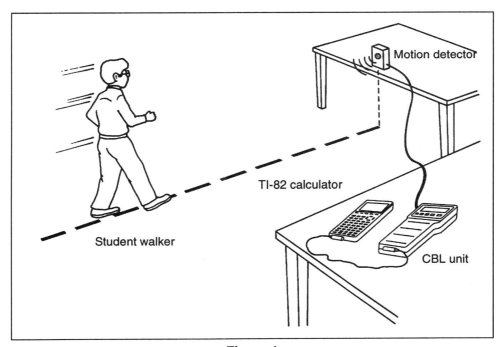

Figure 1

INSTRUCTIONS:

1. Set up the motion detector on a table or desk, as shown in Figure 1. The detector should be aimed at the waist or chest of an average student. Use the meter stick to measure ½-meter intervals from the detector. Mark each interval on the floor with a piece of masking tape. Write the distance from the detector on the masking tape.

2. Run the program MATCHIT on your TI-82 calculator.

3. Follow the directions on the TI-82 screen to complete the activity.

ACTIVITY DATA:

One of three distance vs. time graphs will be generated. The scale markers on the vertical axis of the graph are the ½-meter marks. Once you have a good fit, select [QUIT] from the menu options. This will produce a plot of your motion data.

When you are satisfied with your results, sketch your resulting distance vs. time graph on the axes provided in Figure 2.

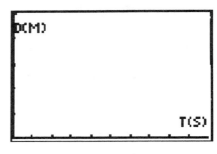

Figure 2

QUESTIONS:

You will now write an equation that describes the motion shown in the plot. You will first write an equation for each section of the graph and then put the pieces together to write a piece-wise defined equation.

1. Press [TRACE] and record the X and Y coordinates of the first point on the graph as X_1 and Y_1. Trace to the end of the first section of the graph and record the X and Y coordinates of this point as X_2 and Y_2.

X_1		Y_1	
X_2		Y_2	

2. The slope of a line, m, is given by the formula shown below. Use the formula to calculate the slope of the line between the points given. Include the units of the slope when you record your answer.

$$m = \frac{Y_2 - Y_1}{X_2 - X_1}$$

$m = $ _____

Name _____

3. The equation for this section of the graph can be found using the equation $y = mx + b$, where m is the slope and b is the y-intercept. Since the graph begins at Y_1 and X is zero at this point, $b = Y_1$. Write the equation for the first section of the graph below.

_____

Check to see that this equation does fit the data for the first section of the graph. Press Y=. Enter the equation in the Y_1 function register and press GRAPH. If the equation does not match the data for the first section of the graph, make adjustments to m or b so that it gives a better fit.

4. Press Y= and turn off the equation in Y_1 by moving the cursor over the equal sign and pressing ENTER. When the equal sign is no longer highlighted, the equation is turned off. Press TRACE. Use the cursor keys to move to the end of the second section of the graph. Record the X and Y values as X_3 and Y_3 in the table below.

X_3		Y_3	

5. Since this section of the graph is horizontal, the value of Y_3 should be approximately the same as the value of Y_2. Record the value for the slope of a horizontal line. Include the units of the slope.

$$m = \underline{\hspace{3cm}}$$

If this line is extended to the y-axis, what is the value of the y-intercept of this horizontal line?

$$b = \underline{\hspace{3cm}}$$

6. Press Y=. In the Y_2 function register, enter the equation for the horizontal part of the graph. Press GRAPH. If this equation matches the data well, record the equation on the line below. If this line does not match well, make the necessary adjustments and then record the equation below.

_____

7. Press Y= and turn off the equation in Y_2 by moving the cursor over the equal sign and pressing ENTER. Press TRACE and use the arrow keys to move the cursor to the end of the third section of the graph. Record the X and Y values as X_4 and Y_4 in the table below.

X_4		Y_4	

8. Find the slope of the line between points (X_3, Y_3) and (X_4, Y_4). Record the value below. Include the units.

$$m = \underline{\hspace{2in}}$$

9. The point slope form of a line is $Y - Y_1 = m (X - X_1)$. Find the equation of the line for the third section of the graph. Substitute the values of either (X_3, Y_3) or (X_4, Y_4) in for X_1 and Y_1 and solve for Y. Show your work below.

_____

_____

10. Press $\boxed{\text{Y=}}$. Enter the equation in the Y_3 function register and press $\boxed{\text{GRAPH}}$. If the equation does not match the data for the third section of the graph, make adjustments so that it gives a better fit. Record your equation for the third section below.

_____

_____

11. Press $\boxed{\text{Y=}}$. Turn off Y_3. Move the cursor to the Y_4 position. You now want to write a single equation in pieces that models the data for your walk. When you see X_2, X_3, and X_4, enter your values for these variables from the tables above.

Since your data is described by the equation in Y_1 for values of X between zero and X_2, press $\boxed{(}$ $\boxed{\text{2nd}}$ [YVARS] $\boxed{\text{ENTER}}$ $\boxed{1}$ to paste in the variable Y_1, followed by $\boxed{)}$ $\boxed{(}$ [X] $\boxed{\text{2nd}}$ [TEST] $\boxed{6}$ [X_2] $\boxed{)}$. This means graph Y_1 for values of X less than or equal to your X_2 value.

Now you want to add the second part of the graph to the equation. Press $\boxed{+}$ $\boxed{(}$ $\boxed{\text{2nd}}$ $\boxed{\text{VARS}}$ $\boxed{\text{ENTER}}$ $\boxed{2}$ $\boxed{)}$ $\boxed{(}$ [X] $\boxed{\text{2nd}}$ [TEST] $\boxed{3}$ [X_2] $\boxed{\text{2nd}}$ [TEST] $\boxed{\blacktriangleright}$ $\boxed{1}$ [X] $\boxed{\text{2nd}}$ $\boxed{\text{MATH}}$ $\boxed{5}$ [X_3] $\boxed{)}$. This step adds on the value of equation Y_2 for values between X_2 and X_3.

Finally, add the equation for the third section of the graph. Press $\boxed{+}$ $\boxed{(}$ $\boxed{\text{2nd}}$ [YVARS] $\boxed{\text{ENTER}}$ $\boxed{3}$ $\boxed{)}$ $\boxed{(}$ [X] $\boxed{\text{2nd}}$ [TEST] $\boxed{4}$ [X_3] $\boxed{)}$. Press $\boxed{\text{GRAPH}}$ to display the graph. The equation should match the data. If it does not, check the equation in Y_4.

12. Look at the slope values recorded above. What is the physical representation of the slope in each section of the graph?

_____

_____

_____

Name _____

13. Look at the value for the *y*-intercept of the first equation. What is the physical representation of the *y*-intercept?

_____

_____

14. Describe how you had to walk to create the graph that you matched in this activity.

_____

_____

_____

APPLICATION:

1. Jose created a distance vs. time graph by starting at the 2-meter mark on the floor. He walked towards the detector at 0.25 m/s for 4 seconds, stood still for 2 seconds, walked away from the detector at 0.4 m/s for 2 seconds, and then stopped for 2 seconds. Sketch a plot of Jose's distance vs. time graph.

2. What was Jose's ending position?

_____

_____

_____

Name _____ **Date** _____

MIX IT UP   Activity 20

Suppose that a hot drink and a cold drink are mixed together and you would like to predict the temperature of the mixture. To do this, we need to know the temperatures of the drinks before they are mixed, T_1 and T_2, and the amounts of each used in the mixture, V_1 and V_2. A visual representation of the problem is shown below, where T_m represents the temperature of the mixture:

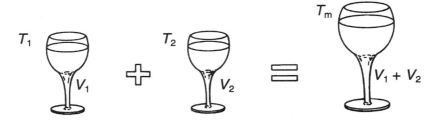

Translated into math language:

$$T_1 V_1 + T_2 V_2 = T_m (V_1 + V_2)$$

In this activity you will use the concepts described above to predict the resulting temperature when two solutions of different temperatures are mixed together. The data needed to perform these calculations will be collected using a pair of temperature probes and the CBL system.

YOU NEED:

1 CBL Unit
1 TI-82 Calculator with Unit-to-Unit Link Cable
2 TI Temperature Probes
1 Graduated Measuring Cup with metric markings (in milliliters, ml)
Hot and Cold Water
2 Large Styrofoam Cups or Coffee Mugs (about 16 oz. capacity)

See the set-up diagram on the next page.

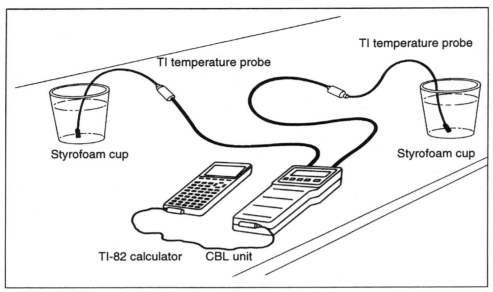

Figure 1

INSTRUCTIONS:

1. In this activity, you will record the temperature of water in two cups, then find the temperature when the contents of the cups are mixed together. To start, label one cup or mug as "Cup 1" and the other as "Cup 2."

2. Fill Cup 1 with 100 ml of cold water (about 10 °C) and Cup 2 with 150 ml of warm water (about 50 °C).

   IMPORTANT: Do not put any ice in the cold water cup.

3. Start the MIXTURE program on your TI-82 calculator.

4. Follow the instructions on the TI-82 screen to complete the activity.

ACTIVITY DATA:

- If you are not satisfied with the data you collected, press [CLEAR] [ENTER] on the TI-82 calculator and start again.

- If you are satisfied with the data, fill in the table below. Record the volumes of water used for the experiment and the temperatures displayed in the "Data Summary" window on your TI-82.

Volumes Used (in ml)		Temperatures Measured (in °C)	
Cup 1 (V_1)		Cup 1 (T_1)	
Cup 2 (V_2)		Cup 2 (T_2)	
		Mixture (T_m)	

Name _____

QUESTIONS:

1. Consider the equation given in the introductory section relating volumes and temperatures for mixed solutions:

    $$T_1 V_1 + T_2 V_2 = T_m (V_1 + V_2)$$

    Solve this equation for the mixture temperature, T_m, in terms of V_1, V_2, T_1, and T_2. Record the result below:

    $T_m = $ _____

2. Substitute the values of V_1, V_2, T_1, and T_2, from the Activity Data table into the equation you found in question 1 above. Solve for T_m, and record the answer below:

    $T_m = $ _____ $^{\circ}$C

3. How does this value compare to the measured value of T_m listed in the Activity Data table? What might have caused the difference between the calculated and measured mixture temperature values?

    _____

    _____

    _____

4. What is the average of the cold and warm water temperatures, T_1, and T_2, used in this activity? Calculate this value and record it below:

    Average of T_1 and $T_2 = $ _____ $^{\circ}$C

    Suppose that you wish to repeat this activity under identical conditions, this time adding exactly the right amount of warm water to Cup 1 so that the mixture temperature, T_m, equals the average temperature value recorded above. Should more or less warm water be added to Cup 1 for this trial compared to the amount you used in the original trial? Why?

    _____

    _____

    _____

5. Exactly what volume of warm water, V_2, should be added to Cup 1 so that the mixture temperature equals the average of T_1 and T_2? To do this, you will need to solve the mixture equation for V_2:

$$T_1 V_1 + T_2 V_2 = T_m (V_1 + V_2)$$

First, rewrite the equation above as an expression equal to zero. Record this equation below:

_____ $= 0$

Substitute Activity Data table values for V_1, T_1, and T_2 into the equation above. Substitute the average temperature value found in question 4 for T_m. Replace the unknown volume, V_2, with the variable X, and rewrite the equation below:

_____ $= 0$

6. The **solve(** feature of the TI-82 calculator makes it easy to solve the equation above for X. This feature finds a solution of an expression set equal to zero, for a specified variable, when given an initial guess. The syntax for this command is :

solve(expression, variable, guess)

To place this command on the TI-82 home screen, press MATH 0. Enter the left side of the second expression you found in question 5, followed by ,. Press X,T,Θ to enter X as the variable you wish to solve for, followed by ,. Finally, enter your guess for the value of X (almost any value will do). Close the parentheses by pressing), then press ENTER to find the value of X. Round this value to the nearest hundredth and record it below:

$V_2 =$ _____ ml

7. How does the value of V_2 found in question 6 compare to the Cup 1 water volume, V_1? Why does using equal volumes of water ensure that the mixture temperature will be the average of the cold and warm water temperatures? Justify your answer algebraically. **Hint:** Let $V_1 = V_2$.

_____

_____

_____

Name _____

EXTENSION:

Repeat the activity, this time starting with equal amounts of water in Cup 1 and Cup 2. Summarize the volumes used and temperatures measured in a data table. Based on your explanation in question 7 above, how might you predict the mixture temperature, given that Cup 1 and Cup 2 contained equal volumes and knowing the temperatures T_1 and T_2? Is your prediction consistent with the measured mixture value?

APPLICATION PROBLEMS:

1. The directions on a box of instant cocoa tell you to prepare the drink by adding 6 oz. of hot water to the package contents. What amounts of cold water (8 $^\circ$C) and boiling water (100 $^\circ$C) should be combined to obtain 6 oz. of cocoa at a temperature of 68 $^\circ$C?

2. Suppose the thermostat of your school's swimming pool malfunctions causing the water temperature to climb to 93 $^\circ$F. The recommended temperature for competition is 78 $^\circ$F. If the pool holds 200,000 gallons of water, how many gallons must be drained from the pool and replaced with tap water (42 $^\circ$F) to make it ready for competition?

3. Some types of mixture problems involve combining solutions made up of different percentages of a substance in order to get a mixture with the desired percentage of that substance. The basic idea is the same as that used in the activity you just completed. Use the space below to solve the following percentage mixture problem:

    Solution A is 5% acid. Solution B is 17% acid. A chemist wants to mix the two to get 500 ml of a solution that is 12% acid. How much of each should be used?

AND NOW, THE WEATHER...   Activity 21

Meteorologists use mathematics to interpret weather patterns and make predictions. Part of their job involves collecting and analyzing temperature data. Important characteristics of the temperature data set are called *statistics*. One statistic you have probably heard the local weatherperson discuss on the news is the day's average temperature. There are at least three different measures of this statistic:

- The *mean* temperature is what we usually think of when we hear the word "average." It is the sum of the temperature values in the data set divided by the number of elements in the set.

- The *median* temperature represents the center data point of the set after all the elements have been placed in order from lowest to highest.

- The *mode* is the most frequently occurring temperature value in the set.

Almost any weather forecast includes a summary of the day's high temperature, called the *maximum* value, and the day's low temperature, called the *minimum* value. The difference between these two statistics, called the *range*, shows the variability or *spread* of the data.

In this activity you will collect outdoor temperature readings over a 24-hour period using the CBL System with a temperature probe. After this data has been retrieved to your TI-82 calculator, you will use the statistical analysis tools of the TI-82 to create your own temperature report.

YOU NEED:

       1 CBL Unit
       1 TI-82 Calculator with Unit-to-Unit Link Cable
       1 TI Temperature Probe

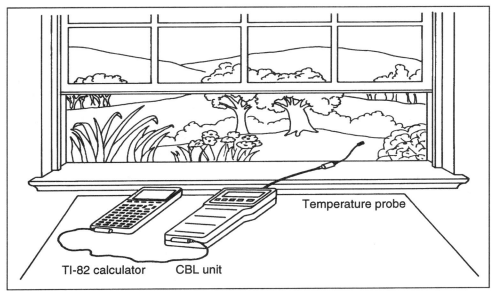

Figure 1

INSTRUCTIONS:

In this activity, you will collect outdoor temperature readings for a 24-hour period. Only the bulb-like end of the temperature probe needs to be exposed to the outside environment.

1. Set up the activity as shown in Figure 1.

2. Place the temperature probe outside a window, with the CBL unit on the inside of the window. *Make sure that the window is not closed tightly on the probe cord.*

3. Start the WEATHER program on your TI-82 calculator.

4. Follow the instructions on the TI-82 screen to complete the activity.

   Note: During this activity, the TI-82 will be disconnected from the CBL. Data collection will start when the [TRIGGER] button on the CBL unit is pressed. The calculator and CBL will be reconnected when it is time to retrieve the temperature data.

5. Use the space provided below to record the starting time for this activity:

Starting time: _____

RETRIEVING THE DATA:

You will know that the CBL unit has finished collecting data when the word **DONE** appears in the lower left-hand corner of the CBL display screen.

1. Start the GETEMP program on your TI-82 calculator.

2. Follow the instructions on the TI-82 screen to retrieve the temperature data from the CBL.

ACTIVITY DATA:

Look at the temperature vs. time plot that appears on your TI-82 screen. If this data does not reflect the actual temperature variations for the 24-hour collection period, you should collect the data again.

- If you need to start again, rerun the WEATHER program on your calculator.

- If your data is acceptable, make a rough sketch of the temperature data you collected in the space provided in Figure 2.

Figure 2

Note that the time values on the horizontal axis are expressed in military time using decimals in place of colons. For example, 9:45 a.m. is expressed as 9.45 and 3:20 p.m. is expressed as 15.20. The vertical line shown on your plot marks midnight; times after midnight are expressed as values larger than 24. For example, 29.30 corresponds to 5:30 a.m. on the second day of the experiment.

Name _____

QUESTIONS:

1. Press ⌷TRACE⌷ and use the arrow keys to move along the temperature plot. The x-values that appear at the bottom of the screen represent military times with decimals in place of colons. Identify at least two time intervals during the 24-hour collection period during which there was a significant change in the temperature. Can you relate these times to specific weather events that occurred during the day such as rain showers, periods of cloudiness, sunrise or sunset?

Time Interval of Rise/Fall	Corresponding Weather Event
to	
to	
to	
to	

2. During this activity, a total of 99 temperature readings were collected and recorded in list L_2. We can find the mean temperature by summing the elements in this list and dividing by 99. To find the sum of list L_2, press ⌷2nd⌷ [LIST] ⌷▸⌷ ⌷5⌷ ⌷2nd⌷ [L_2] ⌷ENTER⌷. Record this value below:

Sum of list L_2: _____

Determine the *mean* temperature by dividing the sum you just found by 99. Record your answer below, rounded to the nearest tenth of a degree:

Mean	

3. What temperature value occurs most often? It is called the *mode*. Before you can find the mode, you need to arrange the temperature readings in order from lowest to highest. To do this press ⌷STAT⌷ ⌷2⌷ ⌷2nd⌷ [L_2] ⌷,⌷ ⌷2nd⌷ [L_1] ⌷)⌷ ⌷ENTER⌷. Press ⌷STAT⌷ ⌷ENTER⌷ ⌷▸⌷ so that the cursor is positioned at the top of list L_2. Press ⌷▾⌷ repeatedly to scroll through the temperature values. Identify the most frequently occurring value or values in the space provided below:

Mode	

4. Remember, the *median* is simply the element exactly in the middle of the ordered data list. That is, the 50th element in the list of 99 readings. To find this value, enter $L_2(50)$ at the home screen and press [ENTER]. Record this value below:

Median	

5. Many statistics can be computed directly using the features of the TI-82. The menu screen shown in Figure 3 is obtained by pressing [2nd] [LIST] [▶]. Use these menu items to compute the mean, median, minimum and maximum temperatures, and record your results in the table below.

   (For example, to compute the mean, press [2nd] [LIST] [▶] [3] [2nd] [L_2] [)] [ENTER].)

Figure 3

Mean	
Median	
Maximum	
Minimum	

How do these mean and median values compare with the ones computed in questions 2 and 4?

_____

Compare your maximum and minimum temperature values with high and low temperature results printed in the local newspaper or quoted on the local weather report. Are your results in close agreement with your local meteorologist's reported values? Justify any discrepancies.

_____

_____

_____

Name _____

6. Determine the *range* (high temperature minus low temperature) and record it in the space below:

Range	

People often listen to a local weather forecast before choosing what they will wear for the day. Would knowing the predicted temperature range for a given day provide enough information for this decision? What other statistic(s) would you need to know?

_____

_____

EXTENSIONS:

1. What if this experiment were repeated three months from today? Indicate how you believe each statistic listed in question 5 would change, if at all. Make a rough graph of temperature vs. time corresponding to these projections. Be sure to include scale markings and axis labels on your graph.

2. Suppose you are designing a travel brochure for your city. Assume that the mean, median and mode temperatures for the tourist season matched the values you found during the 24-hour collection period for this activity. Which of these three statistics would you advertise as the average temperature for your city and why? Explain how your choice might depend on regional tourist attractions.

3. You have been asked to write a weather report for your local newspaper summarizing the 24-hour period during which you collected data for this activity. Use your own words, together with the statistical information you gathered during this activity, to write your report.

Real-World Math with the CBL™ System

Name _____ **Date** _____

JUMP!   Activity 22

How high can you jump? What is the average jump height for your class? How does your jump compare with other jumps? One way to answer these questions would be to measure the jump heights for all the students in your class and then analyze this data statistically.

In this activity, you will use a light sensor and a CBL to measure how long you are in the air during a jump. This "hang time" will be used to calculate the height of your jump. The data set made up of the jump heights for all the students in your class will be analyzed using the statistical tools of the TI-82 calculator. Important features of this data set will be summarized in the form of a special graph called a *boxplot*.

YOU NEED:

      1 CBL Unit
      1 TI-82 Calculator with Unit-to-Unit Link Cable
      1 TI Light Probe
      1 Laser or Laser Pointer

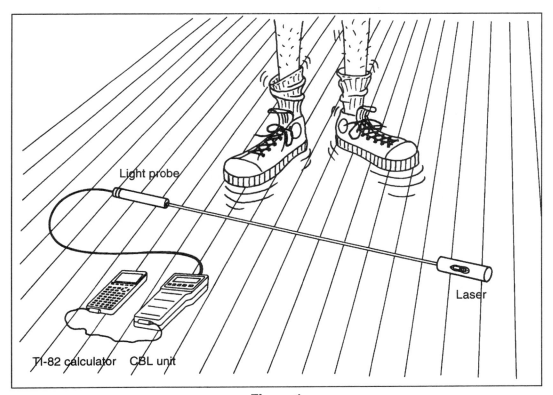

Figure 1

INSTRUCTIONS:

1. Position the laser and light sensor about three feet apart, as shown in Figure 1, so that the laser is shining directly into the sensor.

2. In this activity, you will stand so as to block the beam, then jump straight up and down, as directed. The time the beam is unblocked is detected by the CBL. This "hang time" value will be used to compute your jump height.

3. You will have an opportunity to jump more than once, but only your last attempt will be kept as part of the data set.

4. Run the JUMP program on the TI-82 calculator.

5. Follow the instructions on the TI-82 screen to complete the activity.

QUESTIONS:

1. What are the minimum and maximum jump heights for your class data? To find these values you will first need to order the data values from smallest to largest. To do this press [STAT] [2] to copy the **SortA(** command to the home screen. Then press [2nd] [L_1] [)] [ENTER] to sort the data. Press [STAT] [ENTER] to view the sorted data in list L_1. Use the arrow keys to scroll through the list. Identify the smallest and largest jump heights and record them below:

Minimum height	
Maximum height	

2. There are many ways to describe the "average" value for a set of numbers. One way is to compute the *median*. The median is the middle number of an ordered set of data. If there is an even number of values in the data set, the median is the average of the two middle values.

    Press [STAT] [ENTER] to view the sorted data in list L_1. Use the arrow keys to scroll through the list. Your position in the list is noted in parentheses at the bottom of the screen. Identify the middle value (or the average of the two middle values), and record this number in the space below:

    Median: _____

3. The TI-82 has a built-in feature that can calculate and display a summary of important statistical information for a given list of data. To perform this operation on the data in list L_1 press STAT ▶ ENTER ENTER. Press ▼ several times to move to the bottom of the list of statistics. The minimum, maximum, and median values are denoted minX, maxX, and Med, respectively in the list. Do these numbers match the ones you calculated in questions 1 and 2 above?

_____

Two other important values listed in the statistical summary are the *lower quartile* (denoted Q1) and the *upper quartile* (denoted Q3). These numbers represent the medians of the lower and upper halves of the data respectively. Record these values in the space provided below:

Lower quartile: _____

Upper quartile: _____

4. A special type of graph, called a *box-and-whiskers* plot or *boxplot* for short, can be used to provide a statistical picture of a data set. It gives a graphical representation of the minimum, lower quartile, median, upper quartile, and maximum by displaying a view of the data distribution. To create a boxplot for the jump height data, press 2nd [StatPlot] ENTER ENTER to turn on **Plot1**. Use the arrow keys to move around the screen; press ENTER to highlight the plot features so that your TI-82 display matches the one in Figure 2. Press ZOOM 9 to view the boxplot. Make a sketch of your boxplot in the space provided in Figure 3. Press TRACE and use the arrow keys to move the cursor along the plot.

Figure 2

Label the minimum, maximum, median and quartile values on your sketch.

Figure 3

5. Notice that the *box* part of the plot really represents the middle portion of that data and the *whiskers* stretch to the lowest and highest numbers in the data set. The size and location of the box tell us certain things about the data. A large box indicates that the data is spread out, while a smaller box means the data is clustered. Discuss the size and location of the box part of your plot; describe how it relates to the jump heights for your class.

_____

_____

6. Is the median located near the center of the box? What does the location of the median line in the box tell you about the distribution or arrangement of jump heights for the middle half of the data?

_____

_____

7. The length of the whiskers on the boxplot gives a hint as to the distribution of the data. If one whisker is significantly longer than the other, we say the data is *skewed* in the direction of the longer whisker. This just means that the data is bunched together near the shorter whisker. Describe the whiskers on your plot. What do the whisker lengths tell you about the jump heights for your class?

_____

_____

8. The nature of a boxplot is sometimes distorted by data values known as *outliers*. An outlier is a number that is set apart from the rest of the data set because it is significantly lower or higher than any other number in the set.

   The presence of an outlier might cause you to think that the data is skewed in one direction or another when it really is not. Press STAT ENTER and use the arrow keys to scroll through the list. Pay close attention to the numbers at the very beginning and very end of the list. Can you identify any outliers in your data set? If so, how does this change your answer to question 7, if at all?

_____

_____

9. Describe how your boxplot would be affected if one of the jumpers had a sprained ankle and was able to jump only 1/2 inch off the ground.

_____

_____

10. Suppose that the highest and lowest jumps were removed from your data set. How would the median, lower quartile and upper quartile values change, if at all?

_____

_____

Name _____

EXTENSION:

Another way to analyze the data you collected in this activity is to create a *histogram*. A histogram is simply a graphical representation of the number of times each jump height or range of jump heights occurs. Press [2nd] [StatPlot] [ENTER] to access **Plot1**. Select **histogram** as the type of plot.

Before you view the histogram you will need to manually fix the viewing window. Press [WINDOW]. Choose a number a few inches less than the smallest jump height for $Xmin$ and a number a few inches greater than the largest jump height for $Xmax$. Let $Xscl = 2$; this will group the jump height data by 2-inch intervals. Let $Ymin = 0$. Choose $Ymax$ equal to half the number of students in your class. Set $Yscl = 1$.

Press [GRAPH] to view the histogram. You may wish to adjust the window settings after you view the plot.

Use your own words to describe the data features summarized in this graph. Are the statistical features depicted in the histogram consistent with those shown in the boxplot you created earlier? Discuss the similarities and differences between these two plots. What are some advantages and disadvantages to using each type of plot to describe a set of data?

_____

_____

_____

_____

_____

_____

_____

_____

Name _____   **Date** _____

STAY TUNED   Activity 23

Sound travels through the air much like small ripples travel across a pond. If you throw a rock into a calm pond, the water around the point of entry begins to move up and down causing ripples to travel outward. If these ripples come across a small floating object such as a leaf, they will cause it to vibrate up and down on the water. Sound is produced by the vibration of an object. These vibrations produce pressure oscillations in the surrounding air which travel outward much like the ripples on the pond. When the pressure waves reach the eardrum, they cause it to vibrate. These vibrations are then translated into nerve impulses and interpreted by people as sounds.

These pressure waves are what we usually call *sound waves*. The voices and sounds that you hear every day are generally a combination of many different sound waves. The sound from a tuning fork, however, is a single tone which can be described mathematically using a sine or cosine function. In this activity, you will analyze the tone from a tuning fork by collecting data with a CBL and a microphone.

YOU NEED:

       1 CBL Unit
       1 TI-82 Calculator with Unit-to-Unit Link Cable
       1 Vernier Microphone/Amplifier
       1 Tuning Fork

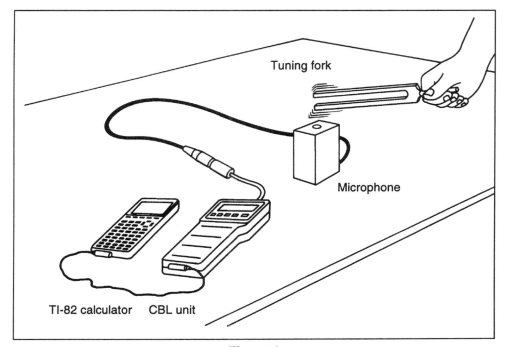

Figure 1

INSTRUCTIONS:

Note: When using sample data, be sure mode is in radians.

1. Run the TUNED program on your TI-82 calculator.

2. Follow the directions on the TI-82 screen to complete the activity.

ACTIVITY DATA:

Your data should be a sinusoidal curve centered about the x-axis.

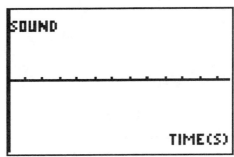

Figure 2

- If you are not satisfied with your data, press [CLEAR] [ENTER] to perform another trial.

- If you are satisfied with your data, make a sketch of the sound vs. time graph on the axis provided in Figure 2.

QUESTIONS:

1. On your TI-82, press [Y=] and move the cursor to the first unused function register. Type the equation $Y = A \cos B(X - C)$, then turn it off by moving the cursor over the equal sign and pressing [ENTER]. You will now find values for A, B, and C which will produce a model that fits your data.

2. The variable A represents the *amplitude* or vertical stretch of the sinusoidal curve that models this data set. Since the curve is centered about the x-axis, the amplitude is the equal to the maximum value of the graph. To find this value, press [TRACE]. Use the arrow keys to move the cursor to one of the apparent maximum values of the data set. Store the y-value of this point as A by pressing [ALPHA] [Y] [STO▸] [ALPHA] [A] [ENTER]. Record the value of A below.

$$A = \underline{\hspace{2cm}}$$

3. For any type of wave, the shortest time interval in which the motion repeats itself is known as the *period*. In other words, the period is the time for one complete cycle of the curve. One method of calculating the period of your sound wave is to find the time between two consecutive maximum or minimum points. Press [TRACE]. Use the arrow keys to move the cursor to any maximum other than the last one. Press [X] [ENTER] to place the x-value of this point on the home screen. Press [TRACE] and then use the arrow keys to move the cursor to the next maximum point on the curve. Press [X] [-] [2nd] [ANS] [ENTER]. This difference in the time values represents the period. Record the value of the period below:

Period \underline{\hspace{2cm}}

4. In your model, the variable B represents the number of cycles that data completes over the course of the natural period of the function. The natural period of the cosine function is 2π. Therefore,

$$B = \frac{2\pi}{Period}$$

Once you calculate the value, store it as B by pressing the value of B followed by $\boxed{\text{STO►}}$ $\boxed{\text{ALPHA}}$ [B] $\boxed{\text{ENTER}}$. Record the value of B below.

$$B = \underline{\hspace{2cm}}$$

5. The value of C represents the horizontal shift of the data. When no shift is involved ($C = 0$), the graph of cosine begins with a maximum value at time zero. To find the shift of your data, press $\boxed{\text{TRACE}}$, then use the arrow keys to move the cursor to any maximum value. Store this x-value as C by pressing [X] $\boxed{\text{STO►}}$ $\boxed{\text{ALPHA}}$ [C] $\boxed{\text{ENTER}}$. Record the value of C below.

$$C = \underline{\hspace{2cm}}$$

6. Press $\boxed{\text{Y=}}$ and move the cursor back over the equal sign of your equation. Press $\boxed{\text{ENTER}}$ to turn the equation on, then press $\boxed{\text{GRAPH}}$ to see the data and your model on the same screen. If your model produces a graph which fits the data, record your equation below. If the graph does not fit the data, make adjustments to the variables A, B, or C until your equation does match the data. Record your final equation below.

$$Y = \underline{\hspace{6cm}}$$

7. The *frequency* of a sound wave is the number of cycles per second. The period of a sound wave is the number of seconds per cycle. Explain the relationship between frequency and period.

_____

_____

Use the period to calculate the frequency of the sound wave and record it below.

$$Frequency = \underline{\hspace{3cm}}$$

8. Standard tuning forks are imprinted with their frequency. Check the tuning fork that you used in this activity and record its frequency below.

$$Tuning\ fork\ frequency = \underline{\hspace{3cm}}$$

How does this compare with the frequency you found in question 7? Explain possible reasons for any discrepancies.

_____

_____

_____

9. The amplitude of a sound wave increases with the loudness of the sound. Explain how you could alter the value of A if you repeated this investigation.

_____

_____

10. *Pitch* is associated with the frequency of the tuning fork. A higher pitched tone would have a higher frequency. Explain how your graph would change if you used a tuning fork of higher frequency.

_____

How would the value of the period change if the frequency were higher? Explain your reasoning clearly.

_____

_____

11. How many different values of C are possible in order to match this graph? Explain your reasoning. Find another value of C that will work and record it below. Check this in your equation, and discuss your reasoning.

_____

_____

12. What changes could you make to fit your equation with a sine curve without returning to the graph? Record the adjustments to any variables. Check your changes by pressing and changing the *cos* to *sin* in your equation. Record the final equation below and your reasons for making changes.

_____

_____

$Y =$ _____

Name _____ Date _____

WALK THIS WAY   Activity 24

A common formula used to solve *rate problems* in mathematics is:

$$distance = rate * time$$

where *rate* refers to the speed of a moving object. This formula is valid provided that the object moves at a constant speed.

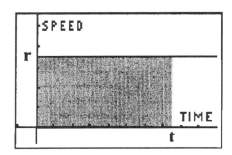

Figure 1. Speed vs. time plot for an object moving at a constant rate.

Consider a speed vs. time graph for an object moving at a constant rate, as depicted in Figure 1. The distance, d, traveled by the object in time, t, is $d = r * t$, where r is the object's rate or speed. Graphically, this distance equals the area of the shaded rectangular region shown in Figure 1.

The area interpretation of distance can be applied even when an object's speed is not constant, as shown in Figure 2a. The total distance traveled can be approximated by summing the shaded rectangular regions shown in Figure 2b. The distance approximation becomes better as the width of the rectangular strips is made smaller and smaller until finally, we obtain the actual distance traveled—the total area under the curve, as shown in Figure 2c. This so-called *limiting process* is a very important idea used in advanced math studies.

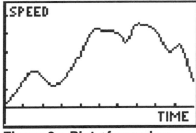

Figure 2a. Plot of speed vs. time.

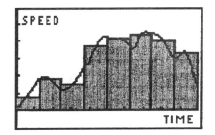

Figure 2b. Distance traveled is approximated by the sum of the rectangular areas.

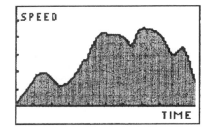

Figure 2c. Exact distance traveled equals the total area under the speed vs. time curve.

In this activity, you will use a CBL system and a sonic motion detector to verify the area interpretation of distance described above.

YOU NEED:

        1 CBL Unit
        1 TI-82 Calculator with Unit-to-Unit Link Cable
        1 Vernier CBL Motion Detector

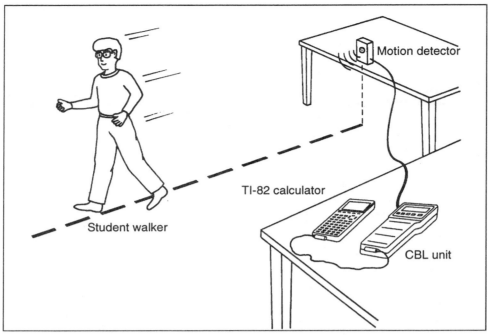

Figure 3

INSTRUCTIONS:

1. In this activity, you will walk in front of a motion detector to create plots of distance and speed as functions of time. (See Figure 3.)

   IMPORTANT: After the CBL is activated, walk *away* from the motion detector. Do not change direction while the CBL is sampling. Try to vary your speed as you move away from the detector.

2. You will have exactly five seconds to collect the motion data.

3. Start the WALK program on your TI-82 calculator.

4. Follow the directions on the TI-82 screen to complete the activity.

ACTIVITY DATA:

Start the GRAPHS program on your TI-82 calculator. Press ① to select **Distance-Time** from the Plot Options Menu and display a plot of distance vs. time for the motion you recorded. Your plot should show distance values that are continuously increasing.

- If you are dissatisfied with your data, run the WALK program and start again.

- If you are satisfied with your data, sketch your plot in Figure 4.

Figure 4

Name _____

Press CLEAR ENTER to return to the Plot Options Menu. Press 2 to select **Speed-Time** and display a plot of speed vs. time for the motion data you recorded. Your plot should show speed values that vary in magnitude but are always above the horizontal time axis. Sketch your plot in the space in Figure 5. Include the axes on your sketch.

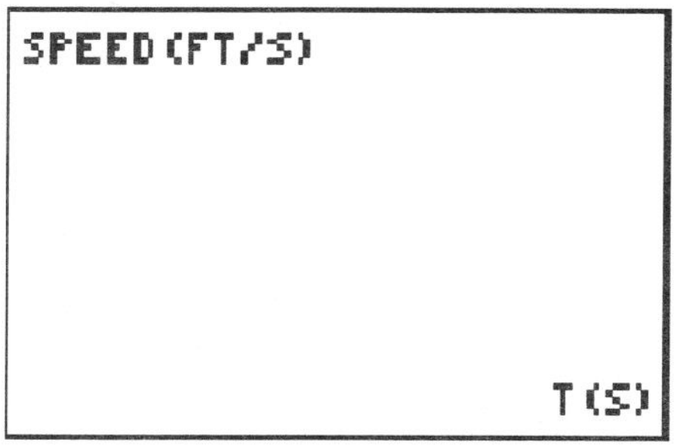

Figure 5

QUESTIONS:

1. Press CLEAR ENTER to return to the Plot Options Menu. Press 1 to select the **Distance-Time** option. Press TRACE and use the arrow keys to move along the plot. The x-values shown on the bottom of your calculator screen are times and the y-values are distances. Determine the starting distance and the ending distance and record these values below, rounding to the nearest hundredth:

    Starting distance = _____ ft.

    Ending distance = _____ ft.

    Subtract these distances to find the total distance walked. Record this value below:

    Total distance = _____ ft.

2. One way to approximate the total distance traveled using the speed vs. time curve is to divide the region under this curve into rectangular sections and sum the areas of these rectangles.

    You will divide the region under the speed vs. time curve into four rectangular sections. To do this, start the GRAPHS program again and press 3 to select **Rectangles** from the Plot Options Menu. Enter **4** when prompted for the number of rectangles. Record the resulting plot in Figure 6. Include the axes on your sketch.

Figure 6

3. Notice that the rectangles divide the horizontal time axis into four equal parts. If the total time for data collection in this activity was 5 seconds, what is the width of each of the four rectangles? Record your answer below, rounding to the nearest hundredth:

Rectangle width = _____ seconds

4. a. Press [TRACE] [▲] to position the cursor at the top of the first rectangle. The *y*-value displayed at the bottom of the calculator screen is the height of the rectangle. Use the [◄] and [►] keys to move from rectangle to rectangle. Record the four rectangle heights in the first column of the table below, rounding to the nearest hundredth.

   b. To find the area of each rectangle, multiply its height by the width value you found in question 3. Record these areas in the second column of the table below.

Rectangle Heights (in feet per second)	Rectangle Areas = Height * Width (in feet)

5. Sum the rectangular areas in the second column of the table above. Record the area sum in the space below:

Area sum = _____ ft.

How does this value compare to the total distance computed in question 1?

_____

_____

6. What would happen if more rectangles were used for the distance approximation? Run the GRAPHS program again. Press [3] to select **Rectangles** from the Plot Options Menu. This time, enter **8** when prompted for the number of rectangles. Record the resulting plot in Figure 7. Include the axes on your sketch.

Figure 7

Name _____

7. The rectangles divide the time axis into eight equal parts. Remember, the total time for data collection in this activity was 5 seconds. What is the width of each rectangle? Record your answer below, rounded to the nearest hundredth:

   Rectangle width = _____ seconds

8. Press TRACE ▲ to position the cursor on the first rectangle. Use the ◄ and ► keys to move from rectangle to rectangle. Record the rectangle heights in the first column of the table below, rounding to the nearest hundredth. To find the area of each rectangle, multiply its height by the width value you found above. Record these areas in the second column of the table below.

Rectangle Heights (in feet per second)	Rectangle Areas = Height * Width (in feet)

Sum the rectangular areas in the second column of the table. Record the area sum in the space below:

   Area sum = _____ ft.

How does this value compare to the total distance computed in question 1?

_____

_____

9. Start the GRAPHS program again and press ③ to select **Rectangles** from the Plot Options Menu. Enter **15** when prompted for the number of rectangles. Notice that when the number of rectangles used is large, the sum of the rectangular areas is computed automatically and displayed at the bottom of the calculator screen. Record this value in the second column of the table below. Round the answer to the nearest hundredth. Repeat this procedure for each of the numbers specified in the first column of the table.

Number of Rectangles	Area Sum (in feet)
15	
30	
100	

How do the area values compare with the total distance computed in question 1? In general, how is the approximation affected by the number of rectangles used?

_____

_____

10. Normally, area values are expressed in square units, such as square feet, ft². Notice that the areas you computed in this activity were in units of feet, not square feet. Explain why this is so.

_____

_____

11. In your own words, summarize the process by which the distance a person walks can be determined using a speed vs. time graph.

_____

_____

EXTENSION:

Repeat the activity, this time walking back and forth in front of the motion detector while the CBL is sampling. How does changing the direction of motion during data collection affect the method for computing the total distance traveled using a distance vs. time graph? Is the area interpretation of distance still valid in this case? Explain why or why not.

Name _____ **Date** _____

FUNNEL VOLUMES   Activity 25

Consider a situation in which water is allowed to drain from a funnel. How is the volume of water changing with time? At what rate is the water level decreasing? How long will it take for the funnel to drain completely? These are a few questions that can be investigated by collecting volume data for a draining funnel then developing a mathematical model to describe this data.

In this activity, you will use a force probe to measure the weight of a water-filled funnel as it drains. Since the density of water is known, its volume can be computed directly. The volume vs. time data can be retrieved to a TI-82 graphics calculator and analyzed using the calculator's statistical features.

YOU NEED:

      1 CBL Unit
      1 TI-82 Calculator with Unit-to-Unit Link Cable
      1 Vernier Student Force Probe with CBL-DIN Adapter
      1 Stopwatch
      1 Funnel
      1 Cup or Bucket to catch the draining water
      String
      Water

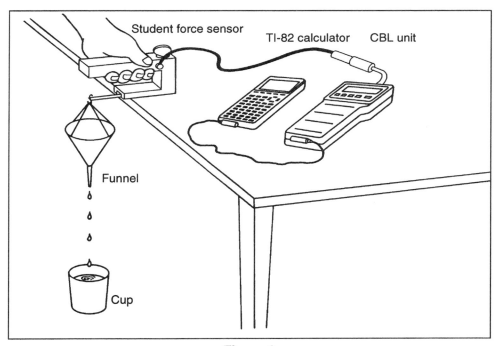

Figure 1

INSTRUCTIONS:

1. Make two small holes on opposite sides of the funnel near the top rim. Thread a piece of string through the holes, then tie the ends of the string together to create a handle as shown in Figure 1.

2. Place a cup or bucket on the floor to catch water as it drains from the funnel.

3. Block the funnel hole with your finger and fill the funnel with water. How long will it take for the funnel to drain? Remove your finger from the funnel hole and start the stopwatch simultaneously.

4. Write your drain time in the space below. You will be prompted for this value by the FUNNEL program on the TI-82.

   Collection time: _____ seconds

4. Start the FUNNEL program on your TI-82 calculator.

5. Follow the instructions on the TI-82 screen to complete the activity.

ACTIVITY DATA:

Your volume vs. time plot should appear to be linear.

- If you are not satisfied with your data, press [CLEAR] [ENTER] and start again.

- If you are satisfied with your data, make a rough sketch of the volume vs. time data that you collected on the axes in Figure 2. Be sure to show the vertical and horizontal axes on your sketch.

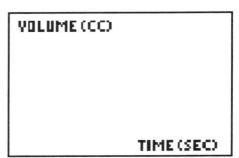

Figure 2

QUESTIONS:

1. Press [TRACE] and use the arrow keys to move the cursor along the data points. Choose any two points (X_1, Y_1) and (X_2, Y_2) along the data plot and record them in the table below. Round these values to the nearest hundredth.

X: time (sec)	Y: volume (cc)

Name _____

2. Use the points in the table in question 1 to compute the slope, m, of the volume vs. time line. Record it below:

$$m = \frac{Y_2 - Y_1}{X_2 - X_1} = \underline{\hspace{4cm}}$$

Why is the value of m negative?

_____

3. You will model the data with a linear equation of the form $Y = mX + B$, where B represents the y-intercept (that is, the initial volume). Press [TRACE] and estimate the y-intercept value in the space below:

$$B = \underline{\hspace{4cm}}$$

Using the values of m and B determined above, write a linear equation that models your data:

_____

4. Press [Y=] and use the arrow keys to move the cursor to the first available function register. Enter the equation found in question 3, then press [GRAPH] to see the data and this line on the same screen. Does it appear to provide a good fit for the data?

_____

5. Determine the x-intercept for the linear equation found in question 3. What is the physical interpretation for this value?

$$x\text{-intercept} = \underline{\hspace{4cm}}$$

_____

_____

6. The TI-82 calculator has a built-in feature that allows it to compute the best-fitting line through a set of data. This procedure is called a *linear regression*. To perform a linear regression on the data you have collected, press [STAT] [▶]. Select **LinReg** or press [5] to copy the linear regression command to the home screen. Press [ENTER] to execute this command. Copy the values which appear on your calculator screen into the matching table in Figure 3.

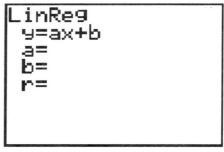

Figure 3

How do the value of a and b in the linear regression equation compare with the m and B values found earlier?

_____

_____

Press [Y=] and use the arrow keys to move the cursor to the first available function register. Press [VARS] [5] [▶] [▶] [7] to copy the regression equation found above into the Y= list. Press [GRAPH] to see the data, the line from question 3, and the regression line all on the same screen.

7. What physical characteristics of the funnel could be changed to affect the rate at which the volume of water in the funnel is changing with time?

_____

_____

CALCULUS EXTENSION:

Determine the radius-to-height ratio for the funnel you used. Write an equation relating volume, V and height, h. Differentiate this equation with respect to time. Use your volume vs. time graph to find dV/dt. Substitute this value into the differential equation. Solve for h as a function of t.

Use this relationship to determine when the water level is half its initial value. To test your answer, plug the hole and re-fill the funnel. Unplug the hole and activate a stopwatch simultaneously. Re-plug the hole when the stopwatch reading matches the time you computed above. Is the height of the water in the funnel approximately half its initial value?

_____

_____

_____

FROM HERE TO THERE   Activity 1

ACTIVITY NOTES:

1. Two calculators, two CBLs, and two motion detectors are needed for this activity. It is important that the students correctly designate the x- and y- calculators when prompted in the DISTFORM program.

2. Be sure to arrange the detectors so that their faces are parallel to the edges of the pattern sheet.

3. When tracing the pattern, remind the students to hold the dowel rod near the top, keeping hands and elbows out range of the motion detectors. Students should start and end the tracing at point A.

SAMPLE DATA:

See Figure 2 on the right.

$A = (56.1, 63.9)$, $B = (60.1, 54.0)$, $C = (50.5, 60.6)$,
$D = (60.9, 60.5)$, $E = (51.9, 54.1)$

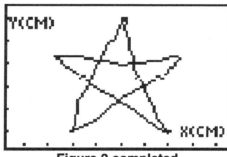

Figure 2 completed

ANSWERS TO QUESTIONS:

1. Lengths using the distance formula: $AB = 10.7$ cm, $BC = 11.6$ cm, $CD = 10.4$ cm, $DE = 11.04$ cm, $EA = 10.6$ cm. Lengths found by measurement: $AB = 11.2$ cm, $BC = 11.2$ cm, $CD = 10.6$ cm, $DE = 11.1$ cm, $EA = 11.0$ cm.

2. The measured and calculated distance values are in close agreement. The measured values are more accurate because the calculated values depend on the data points traced with the dowel rod, which may not have followed the pattern exactly.

3. The total path length = 10.7 + 11.6 + 10.4 + 11.04 + 10.7. This equals 54.44 cm.

4. X-coordinates are the distance of the front side of the dowel rod from the motion detector pointing along the x-axis.

5. Y-coordinates are the distance of the front side of the dowel rod from the motion detector pointing along the y-axis.

6. The measured distance from the y-detector to point $A = 63.9$ cm. This value matches the value of the y-coordinate at point A and is consistent with the physical interpretation in question 5.

MAKING CENTS OF MATH   Activity 2

ACTIVITY NOTES:

1. Be sure that the force probe is positioned as shown in the setup diagram and that nothing is in contact with the metal bar except for the penny bucket hanging from it.

2. Each time pennies are added to the bucket, students should wait until it stops swinging before pressing [ENTER] to collect the mass data. Be sure that nothing is touching the penny bucket while readings are being taken.

3. Mass readings obtained from the CBL are only accurate to within one or two grams. Consequently, students are asked to round their answers to the nearest whole gram in this activity.

4. Pennies minted between 1959 and 1981 are composed of 95% copper and 5% zinc with an average mass of 3.11 grams. Pennies minted from 1983 on are composed of 99.2% zinc and 0.8% copper with an average mass of 2.50 grams.

SAMPLE DATA:

See Figure 2 on the right.

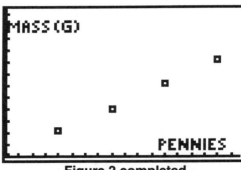

Figure 2 completed

ANSWERS TO QUESTIONS:

1. slope $m = 2.57$.

2. x = the number of pennies being massed.

3. y = the total mass of the pennies in the cup.

4. total mass; number of pennies.

5. mass; penny.

6. $b = 0$; $y = 2.57x$.

7. Yes, the equation provides a good fit.

8. $a = 2.566$; $b = -0.369$; $r = 0.999$. The values are consistent.

9. The slope would be greater, producing a steeper graph.

10. the mass of one quarter.

POOL PLUNGE | Activity 3

ACTIVITY NOTES:

1. Be sure that the tubing is securely connected to the pressure sensor valve. Tubing that is connected and disconnected from the valve often tends to stretch, causing a loose connection. If this occurs, cut a few inches from the end of the tubing and reconnect it to the valve. Watch the tubing to make sure it does not kink and distort the pressure values.

2. Note that the unit for pressure measurement is *pounds per square inch*, abbreviated *psi*. As a general rule of thumb, pressure increases by about 4.3 psi for every depth increase of 10 feet, and the pressure at the surface of the water is about 14.7 psi. Accordingly, the pressure vs. depth equation should be close to *p = 0.43 d + 14.7*. You may wish to have your students compare their findings with this theoretical result.

3. If you do not have access to a pool, you can still perform this activity. It is possible to use a section of garden hose as a "portable" pool. Just cap off one end of the hose and fill the hose with water. Hold the uncapped end in the air as high as you can. The height to which the uncapped end of the hose is raised is the depth of your "portable" pool. Start the POOL program on your TI-82 and enter this height when prompted for pool depth in the program. Carefully lower the plastic tubing into the hose, as if you were lowering it into a real pool. Follow the on-screen instructions to complete the activity.

SAMPLE DATA:

See Figure 2 on the right.

ANSWERS TO QUESTIONS:

1. $X_1 = 3$, $Y_1 = 15.77$; $X_2 = 6$, $Y_2 = 17.00$.

2. $m = 0.41$.

3. $B = 14.7$; y = *0.41x + 14.7*.

4. Yes, the fit is very good.

5. Linear regression values: $a = 0.403$, $b = 14.602$, $r = 0.999$. Yes, the values are consistent.

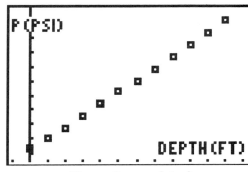

Figure 2 completed

MEET YOU AT THE INTERSECTION | Activity 4

ACTIVITY NOTES:

1. The motion detectors should be positioned about waist-high and about one meter apart from each other for best results. Be sure that the walkers do not get closer than half a meter to the detectors during the collection process.

2. The walkers should try to move as soon as the motion detectors are activated and should not finish their motion before the detectors stop. This will avoid having to make adjustments in the slopes or y-intercepts when formulating the modeling equations.

3. You may wish to repeat this activity for several different walking situations, such as those posed in question 7.

SAMPLE DATA:

See Figure 2 at the right.

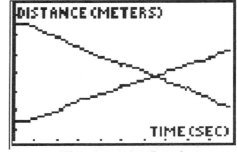
Figure 2 completed

ANSWERS TO QUESTIONS:

1. y-intercept for Walker 1: 3.28;
   y-intercept for Walker 2: .71.

   These values represent the starting distances of the walkers from the motion detectors.

2. Walker 1: 2.40, 2.82, 4.50, 2.31;
   Walker 2: 1.70, .92, 5.40, 1.69.

3. Slope for Walker 1: − 0.24; slope for Walker 2: 0.21.

4. A positive slope corresponds to motion away from the detector. A negative slope indicates motion towards the detector.

   The larger the magnitude of the slope (the steeper), the greater the speed of the walker.

5. Equation for Walker 1: $y = - 0.24x + 3.28$; equation for Walker 2: $y = 0.21x + 0.71$

   The equations are close to the data but do not provide perfect fits. Instead, the equations are parallel to the graphed data.

   Adjusted equations: 1: $y = - 0.24x + 3.38$; 2: $y = 0.21x + 0.61$

6. x-value: 6.16; y-value: 1.90

   The x-value represents the time and the y-value is the distance from the motion detectors when the walkers passed each other. These values compare very closely to the intersection time and location values recorded earlier.

7. Answers may vary. One possibility for achieving a graph in which the plots do not intersect would be for the walkers to both move away from the motion detectors at the same speed while maintaining a constant distance apart. In this case, the plots would be parallel.

   Answers may vary. A graph could be made by the walkers in which the data plots would intersect more than once by having one walker change direction.

STRETCH IT TO THE LIMIT | Activity 5

ACTIVITY NOTES:

1. To stretch and relax the rubber band, grasp it with your fingertips or loop it around one of your fingers. Be sure that the back of your hand is facing the motion detector. While data is being collected, your hand should remain perpendicular to the table surface as it moves back and forth smoothly.

2. It is important to keep tension in the rubber band while data is being collected. Be careful not to over-stretch the rubber band.

SAMPLE DATA:

See Figure 2.

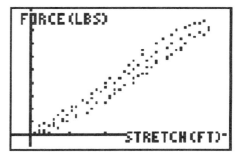

Figure 2 completed

ANSWERS TO QUESTIONS:

1. $K = 1.95$.

2. $x = 0.25$, $y = 0.49$, and $k = 1.96$. Yes, they are consistent. The choice of coordinates affects the values of K.

3. The regression values are: $a = 1.904$, $b = -0.038$, and $r = 0.981$. The a value in the regression equation is in close agreement with the K values computed earlier. The b value should equal zero since no stretch implies no force.

4. The regression equation appears to give a better fit. The $y = kx$ equation is a better direct variation model since it does not include the additional constant term.

5. The graph shows force variations as a function of stretch amount, not force vs. time or stretch vs. time.

6. The plot would have the same general shape, but the K value would be larger.

UNDER PRESSURE   Activity 6

ACTIVITY NOTES:

1. Be sure to attach the syringe to the short piece of tubing included with the pressure sensor for best results.

2. When opening the valve to reset the probe to zero, do not remove the screw completely, just loosen it. Be sure that the valve is securely tightened before you start collecting data.

3. Another way to compute the x*y data products for question 2 involves using the TI-82 list editor. Key in 2nd [L₁] × 2nd [L₂] STO▶ 2nd [L₃] ENTER on the home screen. To view the list of data products, press STAT ENTER and look at list L_3.

SAMPLE DATA:

See Figure 2 on the right.

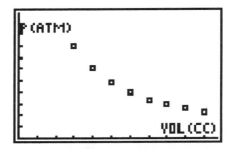

ANSWERS TO QUESTIONS:

1. $K = 24$; $y = \dfrac{24}{x}$

Figure 2 completed

2. A summary of the sample data and data products is shown in the table below:

x	6	8	10	12	14	16	18	20
y	3.9	3.0	2.4	2.0	1.7	1.4	1.3	1.10
x*y	23.4	24.0	24.0	24.0	23.8	22.4	23.4	22

By definition, an inverse relation is defined by $x*y = k$, as noted in the introductory section of the activity.

3. For $x = 2.5$, $y = 9.6$

   For $x = 17.8$, $y = 1.348$

   For $x = 520$, $y = 0.0462$

   For $x = 0.0012$, $y = 20{,}000$.

4. Volume can only get very, very close to zero. Zero volume would imply an unbounded pressure.

5. Increases.

LIGHT AT A DISTANCE   Activity 7

ACTIVITY NOTES:

1. In this activity, intensity readings begin when the sensor is 1 meter from the light bulb. At distances closer than 1 meter, the light sensor may become saturated, giving erroneous readings.

2. If your students have had exposure to logarithms, it may be worthwhile for them to find B algebraically in question 4 of the activity.

3. It is important that all values found in the activity are carried out to four decimal places since rounding may cause the B value to deviate from the expected value of -2.

SAMPLE DATA:

See Figure 2 at the right.

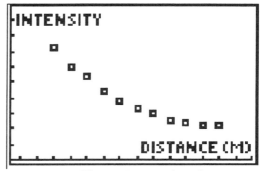

Figure 2 completed

ANSWERS TO QUESTIONS:

1. $A = 0.1815$.

2. $X = 1.1$; $Y = 0.1499$; $0.1499 = 0.1815 (1.1)^{\wedge}B$.

3. $0.1499 - 0.1815 (1.1)^{\wedge}B = 0$.

4. $B = -2.01$.

5. $y = 0.1815 * x^{\wedge}(-2.01)$.

6. The model fits the data very well; the curve is in close agreement with the data.

7. A brighter bulb would increase the value of A, and a dimmer bulb would decrease it. The value of B would stay the same in either case.

8. The A value closely matches the value found earlier, but the B value is a bit smaller in magnitude than the one computed in question 4.

9. The value of B would be - 2 if expressed in the form $Y = A*X^{\wedge}B$. This is consistent with the models found earlier.

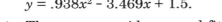

WHAT GOES UP... Activity 8

ACTIVITY NOTES:

1. It is important to provide a well-defined target for the motion detector's ultrasonic beam. If your data plot is not satisfactory, check your cart's target surface. You may need to attach a small piece of cardboard to the cart's front end.

2. Note that the time required for the cart to travel up and down the ramp can be adjusted in two ways: adjust the steepness of the ramp or adjust the cart's initial speed. A round-trip collection time of about 4 seconds is ideal.

3. You may wish to mark the position at which the cart is zeroed with a piece of tape on the board. This will help the students ensure that the cart passes this position as it moves up and down the ramp.

SAMPLE DATA:

See Figure 2 on the right.

ANSWERS TO QUESTIONS:

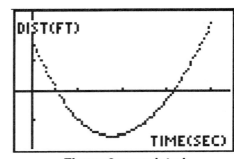

Figure 2 completed

1. y-intercept = 1.5, first x-intercept = 0.5, second x-intercept = 3.2.

2. Product of x-intercepts = 1.6, sum of x-intercepts = 3.7.

3. $a = 0.938$, $b = -3.469$, $c = 1.5$, $y = .938x^2 - 3.469x + 1.5$.

4. The curve provides a good fit.

5. Regression values: $a = 0.863$, $b = -3.230$, $c = 1.506$. They are in close agreement.

6. The cart's maximum distance from the starting point is the point where the distance to the detector is at a minimum.

7. The graph would be inverted; the value of a would be negative.

THAT'S THE WAY THE BALL BOUNCES   Activity 9

ACTIVITY NOTES:

1. Avoid using a soft or felt-covered ball such as a tennis ball because the ultrasonic waves from the motion detector tend to be absorbed by these surfaces. If you have trouble obtaining satisfactory results, try using a larger ball.

2. Be sure that the motion detector cord does not obstruct the path between the ball and the detector as the ball bounces up and down beneath it.

3. To expedite data collection, use three students: one to hold the detector, one to release the ball, and one to run the calculator. For best results, hold the sides of the ball, then quickly move hands outward to release the ball.

SAMPLE DATA:

See Figure 2 (original data) and Figure 3 (selected data).

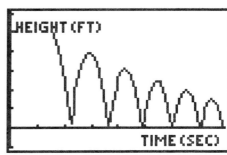

Figure 2 completed

ANSWERS TO QUESTIONS:

1. The x-axis represents time, which is always increasing; it is not related to the physical path of the ball.

2. x-coordinate = 1.46, y-coordinate = 1.96.

3. $A = -16$, $y = -16(x - 1.46)^2 + 1.96$.

4. $a = -16$, $b = 46.72$, $c = -32.15$.

5. $a = -16.04$, $b = 46.83$, $c = -32.21$. Yes, they are in close agreement.

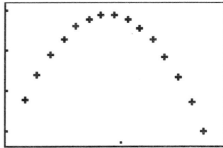

Figure 3 completed

6. For positive values of a, the parabola opens upward; for negative values, it opens downward. As the magnitude of a increases, a vertical stretch is applied to the graph; as the magnitude of a decreases, a vertical shrink is applied.

7. The value of h would increase; the value of k would decrease.

CHILL OUT   Activity 10

ACTIVITY NOTES:

1. The water used for this activity should be very hot (at least 120 degrees), but does not need to be boiling. In most cases, hot tap water should be sufficient. Students should work quickly to collect the data before the water cools too much.

2. Other liquids such as coffee or tea may be used in place of water.

3. Remember that the graph is asymptotic to the room temperature value. When determining room temperature (the C value), position the horizontal marker so that it is one or two pixels below the minimum temperature value shown in the viewing window.

4. The CBL can be placed in multimeter mode to read the room temperature at the beginning of the experiment. Plug the temperature probe into Channel 1 and press the MODE key. The CBL is in multimeter mode. The temperature readings are shown in Celsius degrees on the CBL screen. These can be converted to Fahrenheit degrees and used as the room temperature value.

   CAUTION: Be sure to press MODE again to get out of multimeter mode before running the experiment or you will not be able to collect data. Running the CBL programs from the TI-82 will not take the CBL out of the multimeter mode.

SAMPLE DATA:

See Figure 2.

ANSWERS TO QUESTIONS:

1. $C = 70.97$.

2. Y-intercept $= 124.63$, $A = 53.66$

3. $B = 0.98$

4. The values in L_3 represent the difference between the measured temperature and room temperature.

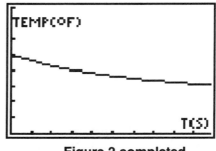

Figure 2 completed

   Linear regression values: $a = 58.176$, $b = .978$, $r = -.997$. The values for a and b should match those determined in questions 2 and 3.

5. Both equations should provide a good fit for the temperature data.

6. The value of B affects the steepness of the curve. For an exponential decay situation, the value of B is always between zero and one. The closer B is to zero, the steeper the curve (that is, the more rapidly the temperature values drop off at the start).

7. The value of B must be less than one because the graph is an exponential decay model. If B is greater than one, the curve would increase exponentially.

KEEP IT BOTTLED UP   Activity 11

ACTIVITY NOTES:

1. If a 500-ml flask is not available, you may use a 250-ml flask, but reduce the water to 50 ml and use only half a tablet.

2. Remind the students to take care when removing the stopper from the flask following the data collection. An alternate way to release the pressure is by opening the valve on the pressure sensor and then closing it back again.

3. The active, gas producing ingredient in the effervescent tablet is baking soda or sodium bicarbonate, as named on the antacid package. Antacids that do not contain this ingredient should not be used for this activity.

SAMPLE DATA:

See Figure 2.

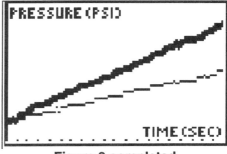

Figure 2 completed

ANSWERS TO QUESTIONS:

1. Room temperature water: 2.90, 15.75, 6.90, 16.83; warm water: 1.90, 15.93, 5.10, 17.73.

2. Slope for the room temp water plot: 0.27; slope for the warm water plot: 0.56.

3. The slopes of the pressure vs. time plots physically correspond to the rates of reaction of the tablets in the water.

4. The y-intercept of the room temperature plot, 14.84 psi, is the value of the starting pressure. This value is the same for both plots because of atmospheric pressure which is ever-present.

5. Equation for room temperature data: $y = 0.27x + 14.84$; equation for warm water: $y = 0.56x + 14.84$. These equations match the data very well. No adjustments need to be made.

6. After several minutes, the plot of pressure vs. time would level off at some pressure value. The pressure would not continue to increase at a steady rate since the effervescent tablet is eventually used up in the reaction and, therefore, no more gases are produced.

7. If the stopper popped off in the middle of the data collection, the pressure vs. time graph would decrease rapidly and would then level off at atmospheric pressure, the value of the y-intercept.

8. For a given water temperature and half a tablet, the plot of pressure vs. time would be a less steep, smaller slope, indicating a slower reaction. Using two tablets would conversely produce a greater slope since more gas would be produced which would increase the pressure.

9. The warm-water plot indicates a faster rate of reaction since it has a greater slope.

10. The rate of reaction increases with increasing water temperature. If you want fast relief from the antacid, the tablet should be dissolved in warm water.

CHARGING UP, CHARGING DOWN   Activity 12

ACTIVITY NOTES:

1. This activity uses a base e exponential function, $y = Ve^{-Kx}$. If you choose, you may ask your students to model their data using an exponential equation of the form $y = a\,b^x$ instead. The values of a and b can then be compared to an exponential regression equation generated by the TI-82.

2. For best results, use a fresh 9-volt battery in this activity.

3. You may choose to discuss how the half-life formula, $t_{1/2} = \dfrac{ln2}{K}$, is derived.

SAMPLE DATA:

See Figure 2.

ANSWERS TO QUESTIONS:

1. When $x = 0$, the equation becomes $y = Ve^0$ or $y = V$. $V = 8.84$.

3. $K = 0.05$.

4. 14.0, $t_{1/2} = 13.9$; close agreement.

5. The value of V affects the starting voltage (y-intercept); the value of K affects the steepness of the curve.

6. The capacitor voltage never reaches zero since the curve is asymptotic to the x-axis.

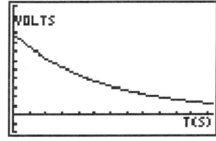

Figure 2 completed

BOUNCE BACK   Activity 13

ACTIVITY NOTES:

1. Avoid using a soft or felt-covered ball, such as a tennis ball, since the ultrasonic waves from the motion detector tend to be absorbed by these surfaces. If you have trouble obtaining satisfactory results, try using a larger ball.

2. Be sure that the motion detector cord does not obstruct the path between the detector and the ball as the ball bounces up and down beneath it.

3. Data collection is expedited using three students: one to hold the detector, one to release the ball, and one to run the calculator. For best results, hold the ball on its side and quickly move hands outward to release the ball.

SAMPLE DATA:

1. See Figure 2.

2. The rebound heights entered into L_4 are: 2.28. 1.85, 1.48, 1.20, 0.965, and 0.781.

4. See Figure 4.

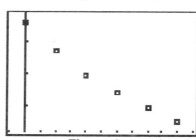

Figure 2 completed

ANSWERS TO QUESTIONS:

1. $H = 2.28$. H is the value of the y-intercept because $P^0 = 1$ and this gives $y = H$ when $x = 0.2$.

2. $P = 0.808$.

4. See Figure 6.

5. $a = -.215$, $b = .826$, $r = -.999$ The equation fits well.

6. $\ln P = -.213$, $\ln H = .824$. These are very close to the values of a and b. They should match up because $\ln P$ is in the same position as a and $\ln H$ is in the same position as b.

7. H is a constant based on the initial height. It will not change if the detector and ball are in the same position. P will decrease because the rebound heights will decrease.

8. 11 bounces.

Figure 4 completed

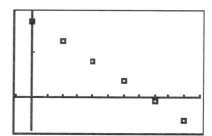

Figure 6 completed

SOUR CHEMISTRY | Activity 14

ACTIVITY NOTES:

1. Be sure to use an effervescent antacid tablet that contains sodium bicarbonate. Many antacids do not dissolve readily in water, making them ineffective for the purpose of this activity.

2. Distilled water, which has a pH very close to 7, is preferable in this activity. The pH of tap water is variable and could change the number of drops of lemon juice required to produce the proper initial condition.

3. When the activity is completed, use distilled water to rinse clean the pH probe so as not to contaminate the storage solution.

SAMPLE DATA:

See Figure 2.

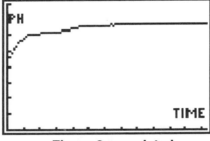

Figure 2 completed

ANSWERS TO QUESTIONS:

1. $C = 4.40$.

2. pH approach value = 6.71.

3. $A = 2.31$.

4. $B = 0.85$.

5. The value of B affects the steepness of the curve.

6. Adding more drops would shift the plot downward. The initial pH value would be lower, lowering the value of C. As well, the A value would be lower since the approach value would be lower.

7. The curve would be steeper if two tablets were used; this would cause the B value to be lower (closer to zero). The A value would be higher, raising the approach value.

8. The B value influences the steepness of the curve; the closer it is to zero, the faster the neutralization occurs.

LIGHTS OUT!   Activity 15

ACTIVITY NOTES:

1. For best results, use a bright light source for Activity Part 1. The actual acts of covering and uncovering the light sensor should be done by moving the thumb very quickly. The time between these events is not so important, provided that it remains relatively constant from cycle to cycle.

2. For Activity Part 2, use a single fluorescent bulb, if possible. If more than one bulb is used, undesirable interference patterns may show up on the plot of intensity vs. time.

SAMPLE DATA:

See Figures 2 and 4.

Figure 2 completed

ANSWERS TO PART 1 QUESTIONS:

1. The plateaus represent instances when the sensor is uncovered; minimums represent instances when it is covered.

2. $A = 0.51$ seconds.

3. $B = 8.57$ seconds.

4. There were 5 cycles completed.

5. The period is 1.61 seconds.

6. The frequency is 0.63 cycles per second.

7. 37.22; this number represents the number of cycles per minute.

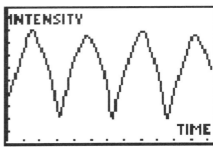

Figure 4 completed

ANSWERS TO PART 2 QUESTIONS:

1. Peaks correspond to times when the bulb is fully illuminated; minimums correspond to times when the bulb is momentarily off.

2. The period is 0.00832 seconds.

3. The frequency is 120.2 cycles per second.

4. Since the polarity switches twice per cycle, we would expect to observe a frequency of 120 cycles per second. This is very close to the calculated value, 120.2 cycles per second.

5. The minimum y-value is non-zero due to the presence of background light.

TIC, TOC   Activity 16

ACTIVITY NOTES:

1. Avoid using a soft or felt-covered ball for the pendulum bob, as the ultrasonic waves from the motion detector tend to be absorbed by these surfaces. A ball with a hole drilled through its center works well as a pendulum bob. Other objects such as a fishing bobber or an empty soft drink can also work well.

2. Students should have some knowledge of sinusoidal curves and some experience with geometric transformations.

SAMPLE DATA:

1. 90.5 cm.
2. 16 cm.
3. 28.3 seconds.
4. See Figure 2.

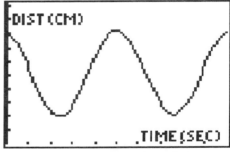

Figure 2 completed

ANSWERS TO QUESTIONS:

1. $A = 16$ cm.
2. Period = 28.3 seconds. The period is calculated by dividing the total time by ten. Ten cycles were used instead of one because the error due to the reaction time of the person working the stop watch is only one-tenth of what it would be for a single cycle.
3. $B = 2.22$.
4. $C = 2.62$.
5. $D = 90.5$ cm.
6. The curve fits well, but slight adjustments give a better fit. These adjustments are due to the difficulty of measuring the accurate position of the pendulum bob with a meter stick. The final equation is $Y = 15.8 \cos (2.22(X - 2.62)) + 90.5$.
7. The values of A, B, and D would not change. The value of C would change because the horizontal shifts needed to fit a sine and cosine curve are different. Students may use a trial and error method to find the new value of C. Some students may reason that the sine curve is the cosine curve shifted right by one-fourth of the period. They may calculate one-fourth of the period and subtract it from the current value of C to find the new value of C. In this case, $2.62 - (2.83/4) = 1.91$. This would be a good method to share in a post-activity discussion for those students who do not discover it.
8. $Y = 15.8 \sin (2.22(x - 1.91)) + 90.5$. The curve fits the data very well.
9. A is the distance that the pendulum swings to either side of the stationary point. B is the number of cycles in the natural period of the function. C is the amount of time that passed between the start of the program and the time the pendulum was a maximum distance from the detector. D is the stationary point of the pendulum or the position of the pendulum when it is at rest.

Teacher Information

SWINGING ELLIPSES — Activity 17

ACTIVITY NOTES:

1. Avoid using a soft or felt-covered ball for the pendulum bob, as the ultrasonic waves from the motion detector tend to be absorbed by these surfaces. A ball with a hole drilled through its center works well as a pendulum bob. Other objects, such as a fishing bobber or an empty soft drink can, also work well.

2. You may wish to explain to students that the sign of the pendulum's velocity is positive as it moves away from the detector and negative as it moves towards the detector.

3. A common misconception when dealing with motion plots stems from the expectation that the graph will exactly match the path of the moving object. In light of this, it might be worthwhile to ask your students why their data plot is shaped like an ellipse even though the pendulum does not follow an elliptical path.

SAMPLE DATA:

See Figure 3 at the right.

ANSWERS TO QUESTIONS:

1. First x-intercept = 1.07

   Second x-intercept = - 1.07

   First y-intercept = 3.06

   Second y-intercept = - 3.15

2. $a = 1.07$, $b = 3.11$.

4. The curves fit the data, as shown in Figure 4.

5. Velocity has the greatest magnitude as the pendulum swings through its lowest point. The velocity is zero (that is, the pendulum comes to rest momentarily) at the highest points of its swing. The y-intercepts correspond to positions where the magnitude of the pendulum's velocity is maximum; the x-intercepts correspond to positions where the velocity is zero.

6. Both a and b would increase, causing the ellipse to dilate.

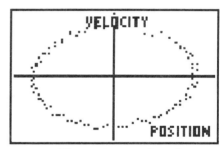

Figure 3 completed

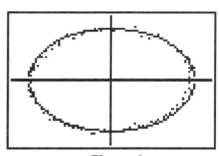

Figure 4

STEPPING TO THE GREATEST INTEGER   Activity 18

ACTIVITY NOTES:

1. Students should be evenly spaced so that the spacing between the steps on the graph is consistent. You could place pieces of tape on the floor at equal intervals and have them line up on the tape if you need to. The students should be spaced approximately 1.5 feet apart.

2. Students should step aside quickly when it is their turn. They should keep their arms at their sides so as not to interfere with the detector.

3. Do not have students lined up next to a wall. The ultrasonic beam spreads as it moves from the detector and may interfere with the wall.

SAMPLE DATA:

See Figure 3.

The values of the constants are:

$A = 1.28$, $B = 0.62$, $C = 2.7$.

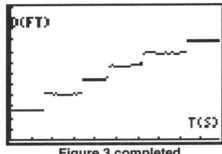

Figure 3 completed

ANSWERS TO QUESTIONS:

1. The C value corresponds to the position of the first student.

2. The value of A corresponds to the average spacing between the students.

3. The value of B corresponds to the reciprocal of the time between student moves.

4. Since the students start farther away, C will increase. A decreases because the students are closer together. B increases since they step off more quickly causing a decrease in time.

5. The correct equation is $y = 0.25 - 0.15\ int\ (1 - x)$. Most students will probably answer $y = 0.25 + 0.15\ int\ x$. Question 6 will have them discover this by checking integer values.

6. The equation $y = 0.25 + 0.15\ int\ x$ does not work for integer values. If a person talks for exactly one minute, the amount charged should be only $0.25. The endpoints need to be adjusted. The equation $y = 0.25 - 0.15\ int\ (1 - x)$ adjusts the endpoints. Students may discover other solutions.

MATCH IT, GRAPH IT | Activity 19

ACTIVITY NOTES:

1. This activity works well when students use the TI-82 screen and an overhead projector so that they can easily see the graph that they are trying to match and adjust their motion accordingly. It will also work in small groups if one member of the group holds the calculator so that the walker can see the graph as she walks.

2. Students should have some knowledge of graphing piecewise functions and the use of the TEST and LOGIC menus.

3. Although the students are matching a given graph, their data points will vary slightly from the given graph. For this reason, they are asked to match the equation to the collected data points rather than the given graph.

ACTIVITY DATA:

See Figure 2 on the right.

ANSWERS TO QUESTIONS:

1. $X_1 = 0$ s, $Y_1 = 0.44$ m, $X_2 = 2.9$ s, $Y_2 = 0.97$ m

2. $m = 0.18$ m/s

3. $Y = 0.18 X + 0.44$

4. $X_3 = 6.0$ s, $Y_3 = 1.04$ m

5. The slope is approximately zero. $b = 0.98$.

6. $Y_2 = 0.98$ m

7. $X_4 = 9.8$ s, $Y_4 = 2.34$ m

8. $m = 0.34$ m/s

9. $Y = 0.34 X - 1.02$

10. $Y = 0.34 X - 1.02$

11. See the Figure 4.

12. The numerical value of the slope represents the speed of the walker. The sign represents the direction. The slope is positive when the walker moves away from the motion detector and negative when he walks towards it.

13. The y-intercept of the first section represents the starting position.

14. I walked away from the detector at a constant speed of .37 m/s for 2.9 seconds, stood still for 2.9 seconds, and then walked away from the detector for 4 seconds.

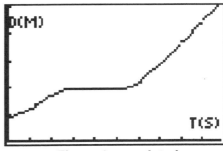

Figure 2 completed

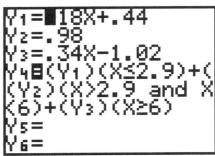

Figure 4

MIX IT UP   Activity 20

ACTIVITY NOTES:

1. There should be a significant temperature difference between the water in the two cups. For best results, one cup should contain water that is above room temperature and the other should contain water that is below room temperature.

2. Generally, cold and hot tap water will work well for this activity. If you choose to use very cold water, be sure to remove any ice from the water before you collect data.

3. You may wish to use different amounts of water than those specified in the instruction section. Be sure that the cups you are using are large enough to hold the combined mixture volume.

4. Have the students work quickly as soon as they begin to collect data. This will help minimize errors due to cooling effects.

SAMPLE DATA:

Volumes used (in ml)		Temperatures measured (in °C)	
Cup 1 (V_1)	100	Cup 1 (T_1)	16.7
Cup 2 (V_2)	150	Cup 2 (T_2)	64.8
		Mixture (T_m)	45.2

ANSWERS TO QUESTIONS:

1. $T_m = \dfrac{T_1 V_1 + T_2 V_2}{V_1 + V_2}$

2. $T_m = 45.56\ °C$.

3. The value calculated using the formula tends to be higher because cooling effects are not taken into account. In this activity various forms of heat transfer cause inconsistencies between calculated and measured temperature values.

4. Average of T_1 and $T_2 = 40.75\ °C$. More. Since we want the resultant temperature to be higher, we must add more warm water.

5. $T_1 V_1 + T_2 V_2 - T_m (V_1 + V_2) = 0$.

    $(16.7)(100) + (64.8)X - (40.75)(X + 100) = 0$

6. $V_2 = 100$ ml.

7. The values are identical. If $V_1 = V_2$, then by substitution, $T_1 V_1 + T_2 V_2 - T_m (V_1 + V_2)$ becomes $T_1 V_1 + T_2 V_1 = T_m (2V_1)$. Dividing by V_1 gives $T_1 + T_2 = 2T_m$, or $T_m = (T_1 + T_2)/2$.

AND NOW, THE WEATHER... — Activity 21

ACTIVITY NOTES:

1. Be sure to have both programs for this activity loaded into your calculator, WEATHER and GETEMP. The first is used to activate the CBL data collection process; the second is used to retrieve the temperature data from the CBL.

2. In this activity, data will be collected over a 24-hour period. Be sure to use fresh batteries for the CBL or use the TI-AC 9201 adapter.

3. For best results, do not place the temperature probe in a location that is exposed to direct sunlight.

4. Note that the data is sorted in question 3. If you wish to view the original data plot, you will first need to restore the data to its original state. To do this, press STAT 2 2nd [L₁] , 2nd [L₂]) ENTER at the home screen.

SAMPLE DATA:

See Figure 2.

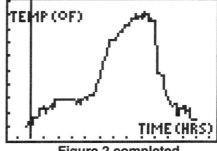

Figure 2 completed

ANSWERS TO QUESTIONS:

1. 31.00 (7:00 am) to 33.45 (9:45 am), rising sun; 41.00 (5:00 p.m.) to 42.30 (6:30 p.m.).

2. Sum of L_2 = 5112; mean = 51.6 degrees.

3. Mode = 44 degrees.

4. Median = 44 degrees.

5. Mean = 51.64, median = 44, maximum = 76, minimum = 35. Mean and median are identical to the values computed earlier. The high temperature was 10 degrees higher than the reported high temperature because the temperature probe was exposed to direct sunlight for part of the afternoon. The calculated low temperature was 6 degrees lower than the reported low, possibly due to the fact that the activity was conducted in a rural location and the reported low was based on city temperatures.

6. Range = 41 degrees; to know how to dress, you would have to know either the high temperature or the low temperature.

JUMP! Activity 22

ACTIVITY NOTES:

1. If you are using a laser pointer, do not keep it turned on manually. Instead, use a twist tie or some strong tape to keep the laser turned on. This will help stabilize the path between the laser and the light sensor.

2. It is important that students interrupt the laser beam path before and after their jump. They should hold their position for a few seconds after they land since the CBL could still be sampling at that time.

3. General features and trends are sometimes hard to detect for small data samples. For best results, use at least 25 jumpers in the class sample. You may wish to combine data sets from several classes for this activity.

SAMPLE DATA:

See Figure 3.

ANSWERS TO QUESTIONS:

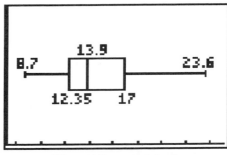
Figure 3 completed

1. The minimum height is 8.7 inches; the maximum height is 23.6 inches.

2. The median is 13.9 inches.

3. Yes, they match. The lower quartile is 12.35 inches; the upper quartile is 17 inches.

4. See Figure 3.

5. The box is relatively small, implying that the data is somewhat clustered between 12.35 and 17 inches.

6. The median line is relatively centered. The middle half of the jump heights are somewhat clustered toward the lower quartile.

7. The data may be slightly skewed to the right. This implies that more students recorded smaller jumps than recorded larger jumps.

8. There are no identifiable outliers for the sample data set.

9. The left whiskers would be extended to the left. The outlier point might cause you to think that the data is skewed to the left when it actually is not.

10. The median would be unaffected. The lower quartile would become slightly larger, while the upper quartile would become slightly smaller.

Teacher Information

STAY TUNED   Activity 23

ACTIVITY NOTES:

1. A tuning fork of relatively low frequency works best. Use tuning forks with frequencies between 256 and 300 hz for best results. A *hz* is the unit of cycle per second.

2. You may want to introduce the term sinusoidal curve to them as a curve which has an equation of the form $y = A \cos B(X - C) + D$. Many books still use the form $y = A \cos(BX + C) + D$. This form is more difficult for most students to understand but could be used if you prefer it.

3. The data is collected for approximately 0.001 of a second.

4. Use a rubber mallet (or the sole of a rubber shoe) to strike the tuning fork to obtain a clean sinusoidal curve.

SAMPLE DATA:

See Figure 2.

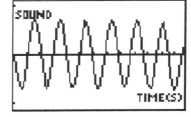

Figure 2 completed

ANSWERS TO QUESTIONS:

2. $A = 0.354$.

3. Period = .00383.

4. $B = 1641$.

5. $C = 0.00311$.

6. $Y = 0.354 \cos(1641(X - 0.00311))$.

7. Frequency and period are reciprocals. Frequency = 261.1.

8. The printed value of the tuning fork was 256 hz. The value is not going to be exact since we used real data points to estimate the maximum values of the curve. To achieve an exact match, students would need to locate the exact maximum values. This is not possible because this is not a continuous function.

9. Answers will vary. Students could strike the fork harder or hold it closer to the probe.

10. A tuning fork of higher pitch would create a graph with a greater frequency. The graph would show more cycles per unit of time.

11. There are infinitely many values that will work for C. Since the graph repeats every time the period of time passes, C could be defined as $C = C_0 + K \ (Period)$, where K is any integer. For the sample data, C could also equal 0.00694.

12. The sine curve is equal to the cosine curve shifted to the right by the period divided by four. To match the curve with a sine curve, subtract 0.00383/4 from the current value of C. The values of A and B remain the same.

WALK THIS WAY   Activity 24

ACTIVITY NOTES:

1. It is important that your starting distance is at least two feet from the motion detector.

2. In this activity, the walker moves ***away from*** the motion detector to create a distance vs. time plot that is always increasing. From this plot, students can compute the total distance the walker travels by finding the difference between the starting and ending positions. If the walker changes directions while the CBL is sampling, this method cannot be used.

3. The rectangular heights are computed at the midpoint of each width. Although the trend is for the distance approximation to get better as more rectangles are used, it is possible for a smaller number of rectangles to give a closer approximation to the total distance traveled.

SAMPLE DATA:

See Figures 4 and 5.

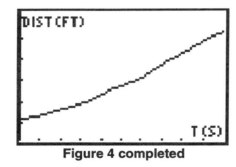

Figure 4 completed

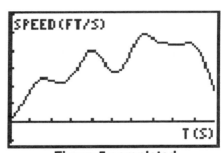

Figure 5 completed

ANSWERS TO QUESTIONS:

1. Starting distance = 3.21 ft;
    ending distance = 7.25 ft; total distance = 4.04 ft.

2. See Figure 6.

3. Rectangle width = 1.25 seconds.

4. Rectangle heights = 0.52, 0.95, 1.13, 1.10 ft/sec;
    Rectangle areas = 0.65, 1.19, 1.41, 1.38 ft.

5. Area sum = 4.63 ft. The distance values are similar, but not in close agreement.

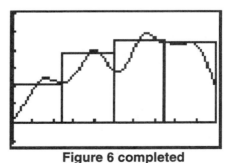

Figure 6 completed

WALK THIS WAY, Continued

6. See Figure 7.

7. Rectangle width = 0.63 seconds.

8. Rectangle heights = 0.24, 0.60, 0.67, 0.93, 0.77, 1.20, 1.08, 0.92 ft/sec;
   Rectangle areas = 0.15, 0.38, 0.42, 0.58, 0.48, 0.75, 0.68, 0.58 ft.
   Area sum = 4.02 ft. This value is in close agreement with the distance found in question 1. This is a better approximation than the one computed in question 5.

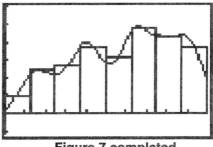

Figure 7 completed

9. For 15 rectangles, total area is 4.05 ft; for 30 rectangles, total area is 3.99 ft; for 100 rectangles, total area is 4.04 ft. The distance approximation typically becomes better as the number of rectangles used increases.

10. The areas are in units of feet because they are computed by multiplying the rectangular heights, in units of feet per second, by the rectangular widths, in units of seconds. The resulting dimension is feet.

11. The distance a person walks can be determined by finding the area under a speed vs. time curve.

FUNNEL VOLUMES   Activity 25

ACTIVITY NOTES:

1. Try to choose the collection time so that the CBL stops sampling just as the water finishes draining from the funnel or slightly before it has finished draining. It is undesirable for the CBL to continue sampling after the water has completely drained from the funnel since we wish to model only the linear portion of the data.

2. Hold the probe and funnel so that both are level while data is being collected. Be careful not to touch the funnel while the CBL is sampling.

SAMPLE DATA:

See Figure 2.

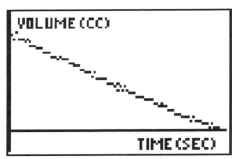

Figure 2 completed

ANSWERS TO QUESTIONS:

1. $X_1 = 0.40$, $Y_1 = 128.74$; $X_2 = 1.28$, $Y_2 = 72.77$.

2. The slope is - 63.60. This value is negative because volume is decreasing with time.

3. $B = 156.72$; $y = - 63.60x + 156.72$.

4. The fit is good.

5. The x-intercept is 2.46. This represents the time required for the funnel to completely drain.

6. $a = - 65.87$, $b = 156.70$, and $r = - 0.998$. They are in close agreement.

7. The size of the funnel hole is the main factor affecting the water flow rate.